The Whole Language Catalog

FORMS FOR AUTHENTIC ASSESSMENT

Lois Bridges Bird

Kenneth S. Goodman

Yetta M. Goodman

SRA/McGraw-Hill

Columbus, Ohio

Project manager: Mary Carman Barbosa
Project supervisor: Rick Brownell
Forms by T&H Graphics
Design by Steve Graydon
Cover by Kurt West

This book features a special lay-flat binding for easy photcopying.

ISBN 002-685705-7

2 3 4 5 6 7 8 9 10 MAL 99 98 97 96 95

About This Book

Professor Dorothy Watson says that "Whole Language teachers share their best," and indeed, within these pages you'll find the best of authentic assessment forms and strategies developed by more than fifty educators. These are forms they've created and use in their classrooms to monitor, document, report on, and evaluate a range of authentic learning experiences in which their students have engaged.

Most of the forms first appeared in *The Whole Language Catalog: Supplement on Authentic Assessment* (1992). As the nature of authentic assessment is evolving, however, many of the forms have changed, reflecting their authors' current understanding of assessment. After receiving numerous requests from the readers of the *Authentic Assessment* supplement to photcopy the forms, we decided that a separate book of forms printed in a full-page format—including several appearing for the first time—would be helpful.

The book is easy to use. Each form is accompanied by a description explaining **WHO** the form is most appropriate for, **WHY** it was created, and **HOW** to use it. Additional information under **WHAT ELSE?** may add to the utility of the form. At the bottom of the page, you'll notice a small **See:**, followed by page numbers that correlate every form with other related forms across the five kidwatching perspectives. Sometimes the forms are several pages long; the page number in the upper-right-hand corner will help you keep track of the length of multi-page forms.

We invite you to photocopy the forms to use in your classrooms. Examine the forms closely. Discuss and debate their utility with your colleagues. You may not like some aspects of some forms. Each represents one teacher or one group of teachers. We didn't impose a single viewpoint on the contributor. Revise and adapt them to meet your unique needs and interests as well as those of your students. Be selective. We've offered several teachers' attempts to assess the same aspects to show alternative views. Whole language teachers are professional decision makers who thoughtfully select materials and use them in ways that make the most sense for them, their students, and their school communities.

Lois Bridges Bird
Kenneth S. Goodman
Yetta M. Goodman

Table of Contents

6 · Introduction

Monitoring: Keeping Track

9 · Primary Developmental Checklist
14 · My Reading Records
· Library Bookmark
· Reading Log
18 · Reading Contract
20 · Home and School Independent Reading, K–5
24 · Children Learn to Read by Reading
26 · Writing Process Overview
28 · My Ideas for Writing
30 · Writing Workshop: Status of the Class
32 · Writing Record
· Writing Workshop Report
35 · Spelling Discovery
37 · My Plans
· Center Committee Plans
40 · Research Contract
· Showing You Know
43 · Planning Grid for Thematic Study

Observing: What's Going On?

47 · Kidwatching Guidelines
49 · Complete Anecdotal Form
· Anecdotal Observation Sheet
53 · Anecdotal Records
55 · Parent Observation
57 · Whole Language Checklist
62 · Profile of Language Arts Outcomes, K–5
69 · Reading: A Guide for Observation
71 · Survey in the Language Arts: Reading/Writing

74 · Cumulative Writing Folders, K–5
81 · A Process Checklist for Writing
· Primary Writing Goals
84 · Observed Reading Behavior
· Fall/Winter Reading and Writing Assessment
· Fall/Winter Math Assessment
90 · Literacy Environment Evaluation
93 · Scale of Writing Development
· Scale of Emergent Reading
· Response to Literature Scale
· Reading Record for Conferences

Interacting: Finding Out

99 · Burke Reading Interview
· Reading Interest Inventory
102 · Reading Environmental Print
104 · Bookhandling Knowledge Task
111 · Child's Concepts of Reading
· Child's Concepts of Written and Pictorial Representation
116 · Reading in Kindergarten
118 · Classroom Community of Readers
· Story Response
121 · Student Writing Survey/Interest Inventory
123 · Peer Conferencing
· Peer Conferencing Guidelines
· Help the Author
127 · Parent-Student Questionnaire
· Getting to Know Your Child
131 · Principal's Goals for the School/Classroom
134 · HOPS: A Holistic Observation Process
138 · Language Arts Review

Analyzing: Delving Deeper

141 · Oral Language Evaluation
143 · Assessing the Spelling Levels of Young Children
145 · Development of Narrative/Expository
· Reading Strategies
· Conventions of Print
149 · Developing a Reading Profile
151 · Miscue Analysis: Forms and Procedures
157 · Miscue Analysis Form
160 · Miscue Analysis: Retelling Summary
163 · Retrospective and Collaborative Miscue Analysis
166 · Editing Checklist
· Peer Editing Checklist
169 · Qualities of Effective Writing
· Outstanding Poetic Qualities
173 · Looking Closer at a Writing Sample

Reporting: Summing Up

175 · Learning Logs
177 · Literature Studies Guidelines
· Literature Response Guide
· Literature Circles
181 · Responding to Literature
· Reader's-Writer's Reflections
183 · Author/Illustrator Study
· Analyze an Author
186 · Book Review: Fiction Books/Non-Fiction Books/Picture Books
· Listening Post Book Review
191 · How Well Did We Work Together?

193 · Self-Evaluation Across the Curriculum: Overview/Math/Science/Language Arts
198 · Responding to Assignments: Self-Evaluation
200 · Fostering Student Self-Evaluation: Focus on Writing
202 · Something to Write Home About
204 · Thinking About Myself as a Learner
206 · Weekly Discussion Group Evaluation
· Evaluation of Discussion Groups
· Evaluation of Group Projects
210 · Learning How to Learn a Second Language
212 · Self-Evaluation in a Graduate Course
214 · Teacher Self-Evaluation
216 · Semester Update
· Parent Response Form
219 · Getting Started with Portfolios
222 · Portfolio Evenings: Guiding Questions
224 · Learning Experiences Form
226 · Portfolio Assessment: Self-Evaluation Sheet
228 · Growth Portfolio Rationale
· Quarterly Growth Summary
231 · My Child as a Language Learner, K–6
235 · Parent Reflection
· Post-Conference Evaluation

239 · Title Index
· Author Index

Introduction

Evaluation, like math and spiders, makes a lot of people nervous.
—Crafton, 1991

Say the word *evaluation* and visions of multivariate analysis and stacks of statistical data may pop into mind. Scary stuff! But evaluation is really a part of life. At home and in the workplace, people are constantly evaluating their own actions. Similarly, we evaluate in the classroom. We watch as Raymond reads *Greedy Cat* out loud, notice how his finger matches the print as he skims the predictable text, quickly assess his developing reading ability, and determine that he would do well with a more difficult book. We pull Arnold Lobel's *Frog and Toad* from the shelf and suggest to Raymond that he would enjoy the adventures of this enterprising duo. Responsive educators have always engaged in this sort of continuous, on-the-spot assessment that is part of the flow of classroom life. We just haven't recognized it as legitimate evaluation stemming from our professionalism—knowing how our students learn, knowing what their needs and interests are, and knowing how to best support students as capable, creative learners.

Educators are realizing that it makes little sense to separate evaluation from teaching and learning. In fact, some suggest that the acid test for evaluation is that it should in some way inform our teaching and help us decide what to do next. When we evaluate kids' learning or ask them to evaluate it themselves, our primary goal is to help them learn more. And herein lies the true meaning, perhaps, of authentic assessment. Assessment is authentic when it is related to student learning, performance, and understanding.

To further demystify authentic assessment, it might help to consider these basic principles:

- *Authentic assessment is an integral part of the curriculum.* Children are assessed while they are involved with classroom learning experiences, not just before or after a unit through pretests or posttests.

- *Authentic assessment is continuous.* It informs every aspect of instruction and curriculum building; teachers learn what to teach as well as how and when to teach it.

- *Authentic assessment occurs over time (longitudinal) and is developmentally and culturally appropriate.* Assessing children's growth is a careful, systematic process that takes place over time in many different contexts that are in constant flux. And it occurs first in the child's home language and is sensitive to cultural variations.

- *Authentic assessment focuses on students' strengths.* Teachers assess what students can do: what they know and how they can use that knowledge to learn. Teachers utilize a variety of strategies that look at both the process of learning as well as the products of learning.

- *Authentic assessment recognizes that the most important kind of evaluation is self-evaluation.* Students and teachers come to understand why they are doing what they do so that they may have some sense of their own success and growth.

- *Authentic assessment invites active, collaborative reflection by both teacher and student.* Students are valued as unique individuals who possess knowledge and who can participate in evaluating their progress. Teachers and students are co-learners, working together to plan, monitor, and assess all learning experiences.

Effective teachers have always been "kidwatchers," continuously monitoring their students' learning and development during their daily classroom contacts. As they try to understand their students, teachers may assume five kidwatching focuses. They are discussed separately in this book, but in most cases when teachers use them, they are overlapping and integrated. Each focus can help confirm the information gained from the others.

Monitoring: Keeping Track

The first kidwatching focus is "keeping track." In which research projects have students participated? What materials did they utilize? Which learning modalities did they explore? Teachers devise a great many ways of keeping track of their students' learning experiences: checklists, inventories, class lists. Children should also be involved; they can account for their learning day through journal entries and lists. Over the course of a year, teachers and students can keep track of and compile a substantial record of learning experiences and accomplishments.

Observing: What's Going On?

We can gather valuable information about our students as learners by standing on the sidelines and observing and listening. We may choose to observe one student working alone, a student as a member of a group, all members of a small group, or the class as a whole. We may record our general impressions or use observation to confirm or reject specific notions regarding the students. Some teachers find setting aside a specific period of time daily for systematic observation of individual students is the most effective way to handle this strategy; others keep a clipboard on hand for continuous note-taking as they see things happen that are worth recording.

Interacting: Finding Out

Interacting with students during the learning process enables us to discover what our students know, feel, and believe. It also challenges them to explore beyond what they are thinking and feeling at the moment. We can question our students informally during small-group or class discussions, or one-on-one; we can raise questions in their journals or conduct a more formal interview. Teachers interact with their students most effectively when they listen patiently and reflectively and ask thoughtful, open-ended questions that nudge children to examine their own thinking: Why do you think so? Is it possible? What if we tried this instead? What if I said ...? I wonder if ...?

Analyzing: Delving Deeper

The fourth kidwatching focus centers on collecting and analyzing in greater depth the artifacts of learning: written stories and reports, sketches and drawings, videotapes of students' presentations, and so forth. These provide students, parents, teachers, and administrators with concrete evidence of progress. As teachers examine artifacts, it's best, if possible, to consider both the content and the process. It also helps if teachers have established specific criteria that they can use to guide their evaluation. Many effective educators involve their students in negotiating and helping to establish the criteria; teachers may need to consider district guidelines as well.

Reporting: Summing Up

At some point, teachers organize the assessment data they have collected in meaningful ways so that they can share it with parents, administrators, and others beyond the classroom door. As the ultimate goal of an evaluation process is self-evaluation for both students and teachers, it is best if students are involved in the process every step of the way. Students should keep records of their own learning experiences and meet with the teacher in conferences to evaluate what they have accomplished and what goals they hope to achieve, planning with the teacher how these are to be met.

In sum, every learning experience is an opportunity for assessment. As teachers continuously evaluate and monitor their students' learning through record keeping, observing, interacting, and analyzing learning artifacts, they can design instruction and create curriculum that will stretch their students' knowledge and expand their worlds.

Reference

Crafton, L. K. 1991. *Whole language: Getting started ...
    moving forward.* Katohah, NY: Richard C. Owen.

Primary Developmental Checklist

WHO?

Using an original form developed by Barbara Rothman, a Southern California kindergarten teacher, Pam Anderson and her colleague Nina LaPeck expanded the checklist for use with their first- and second-graders.

WHY?

Pam wanted to give her students responsibility for choosing, developing, and documenting their own physical, social, and academic goals. She has found that the **Primary Developmental Checklist** provides her students with the support necessary for self-directed goal-setting and learning.

HOW?

Pam explains how they use the form: "We introduce it to the whole class in the second week of school on an overhead transparency. We discuss each item and show the children how to fill in the answers. We talk about 'How do you know when you've accomplished your goal?' For example, a child who has been working to learn her phone number will ask me to test her in some way when she thinks she knows it. Usually I'll wait until the next day or some time after she hasn't just practiced it, and I'll ask, 'Okay, what's your number?' If she knows it, we'll get the marker and write 'completed' on the goal-setting sheet. Then we'll note the date and she'll pick a new goal.

"The children pick their own goals—a social, academic, and physical goal. I help them prioritize; for example, 'You probably want to learn your phone number before you learn addition and subtraction,' and then we talk about why that's important. We talk about how to begin working on a goal, starting with something you can be successful at quickly, and saving the toughest things for later so you get the hang of working on a goal. This year we practiced working on our goals three times a week for at least twenty minutes a day; eventually, the kids learn that the first thing they do when they arrive at school in the morning is to start working on their goals.

WHAT ELSE?

"I determine which children have the same goals so that those kids can work together and help each other. If they want to learn their phone number, I'll write it out for them on a card. How they choose to work on it is up to them. They can choose to write it over and over again. I suggest they use the play phone in the play area and try calling their home. Also, sometimes the children share their goals with their parents and work on them at home as well. It's very exciting, by the end of the year, to have completed all the goals on the form!"

See: OBSERVING p. 84

Primary Developmental Checklist was developed by Pam Anderson, who teaches a first/second grade combination at Orion School in Redwood City, CA.

Primary Developmental Checklist

Name _____ Date _____ Grade _____

PERSONAL INFO. & OTHER LEARNING SKILLS

I know my address ☐ yes ☐ not yet	I know my telephone number ☐ yes ☐ not yet	I know my age and birthdate ☐ yes ☐ not yet	I can write my first and last name ☐ yes ☐ not yet
I can tie my shoes ☐ yes ☐ not yet	I know my right and left hand ☐ yes ☐ not yet	I know the names of these shapes ☐ yes ☐ not yet	I know the parts of my body ☐ yes ☐ not yet
I can cut on a line ☐ yes ☐ not yet	I know upper and lower case letters of the alphabet ☐ yes ☐ not yet	I can print upper and lower case letters ☐ yes ☐ not yet	I know and use the scientific method ☐ yes ☐ not yet

SOCIAL SKILLS AND WORK HABITS

I keep my hands to myself ☐ yes ☐ not yet	I listen when others are speaking ☐ yes ☐ not yet	I am a good speaker before a group ☐ yes ☐ not yet	I can solve my own problems ☐ yes ☐ not yet
I cooperate with others ☐ yes ☐ not yet	I take turns and share ☐ yes ☐ not yet	I help others ☐ yes ☐ not yet	I put things away ☐ yes ☐ not yet

MORE WORK HABITS

I make a plan before I start ☐ yes ☐ not yet	I finish my work on time ☐ yes ☐ not yet	I find important things to do during choice ☐ yes ☐ not yet	I watch and listen ☐ yes ☐ not yet
I can set and work toward my goal ☐ yes ☐ not yet	I follow directions and signals ☐ yes ☐ not yet	I keep my cubby clean ☐ yes ☐ not yet	

P.E. SKILLS

I can jump rope ☐ yes ☐ not yet	I can catch a ball ☐ yes ☐ not yet	I can skip ☐ yes ☐ not yet	I can bounce a ball ☐ yes ☐ not yet
I can hop ☐ R. foot ☐ L. foot ☐ yes ☐ not yet	I can jump rope backwards ☐ yes ☐ not yet	I can balance ☐ yes ☐ not yet	I can throw a ball ☐ yes ☐ not yet
I can throw a frisbee ☐ yes ☐ not yet	I can throw a football ☐ yes ☐ not yet	I'm a good sport ☐ yes ☐ not yet	I can run the baseball diamond ☐ yes ☐ not yet
I can do sit ups ☐ yes ☐ not yet	I can do jumping jacks ☐ yes ☐ not yet	I have strength to cross the traveling bar ☐ yes ☐ not yet	

MATH SKILLS

I can draw these shapes ☐ yes ☐ not yet	I recognize patterns ☐ yes ☐ not yet	I can sort ☐ yes ☐ not yet	I can count __ objects ☐ yes ☐ not yet
I can count by 1's (to 127) ☐ yes ☐ not yet	I can count by 2's (to 106) ☐ yes ☐ not yet	I can count by 5's (to 125) ☐ yes ☐ not yet	I can count by 10's (to 120) ☐ yes ☐ not yet
I can read a graph ☐ yes ☐ not yet	I can match sets ☐ yes ☐ not yet	I can make a pattern ☐ yes ☐ not yet	I can make a graph ☐ yes ☐ not yet
I can do addition to 10 ☐ yes ☐ not yet	I can do subtraction from 10 ☐ yes ☐ not yet	I can give number sentences ☐ yes ☐ not yet	I can recognize and count money ☐ yes ☐ not yet
I can read and use the calendar ☐ yes ☐ not yet	I can tell time ☐ yes ☐ not yet	I can write number sentences ☐ yes ☐ not yet	I can recognize numbers 0-20 ☐ yes ☐ not yet
I can build a double digit number ☐ yes ☐ not yet	I can build a triple digit number ☐ yes ☐ not yet	I know and use > and < signs ☐ yes ☐ not yet	I can recognize random 2 digit numbers ☐ yes ☐ not yet

READING SKILLS

Sh ⌐T S h Ch B Th	ă ĕ ĭ ŏ ŭ	ā ē ī ō ū	
I know beginning consonant sounds	I know short vowel sounds	I know long vowel sounds	I can sound out
☐ yes ☐ not yet	☐ yes ☐ not yet	☐ yes ☐ not yet	☐ yes ☐ not yet
I can skip and go on	I can give a good substitute word	I know punctuation marks	I can read aloud with expression
☐ yes ☐ not yet	☐ yes ☐ not yet	☐ yes ☐ not yet	☐ yes ☐ not yet
I know the characters in a story	I know the setting in a story	I know the plot in a story	I read alone during silent reading
☐ yes ☐ not yet	☐ yes ☐ not yet	☐ yes ☐ not yet	☐ yes ☐ not yet
		I participate in literature study discussions	I finish my literature study homework
		☐ yes ☐ not yet	☐ yes ☐ not yet

WRITING SKILLS

I can edit a story	I share my writing	I use descriptive words	I can write a letter
☐ yes ☐ not yet	☐ yes ☐ not yet	☐ yes ☐ not yet	☐ yes ☐ not yet
I use capitals and lowercase letters correctly in my writing	I can space between words	I use words I know	I use invented spelling
☐ yes ☐ not yet	☐ yes ☐ not yet	☐ yes ☐ not yet	☐ yes ☐ not yet

My Reading Records · Library Bookmark · Reading Log

WHO?

These forms are most appropriate for upper-elementary through middle school students, but with some adaptation and teacher guidance, younger children can record their reading books, too.

WHY?

A monthly reading list allows students to record and receive credit for all of their readings with a minimum of pain. The book list allows students to stop reading a book and still get credit, just as the writing folder may contain incomplete pieces.

HOW?

My Reading Records and **Reading Log** allow children to list what they are reading and to state their opinion about each entry. Both formats give children the option of not completing a book. A monthly list for younger children would use a format that allows them to read the same book over and over. Instead of requiring a report for every book read, Debra Goodman asks students to present at least one book to the class each month. On the back of **Library Bookmark** is a list of possible formats for their presentation, such as: write a report, give a book talk, read a chapter to the class, dramatize a scene from the book, design a book jacket, make a literature map, make a poster advertising the book, etc.

In the Reading Log developed by Maureen White, they also record the title, author, number of pages, and genre of every book they've read, and note whether the book was easy (E), of medium difficulty (M), or hard (H). They mark yes (Y) if they like the book and no (N) if they didn't.

WHAT ELSE?

Debra admits that she has concerns about whether children are honest in creating their lists, and she shares that concern with the students. She lets them know that she is trusting them to tell the truth. But her frequent conferences, reflective journals, literature circles, and in-class reading observations make it easy to verify the list if necessary.

See: REPORTING pp. 181, 187

My Reading Records and Library Bookmark were developed by Debra Goodman, who teaches fifth grade at the Dewey Learning Center in Detroit, MI.

Reading Log was developed by Maureen White, K–8 writing coordinator for Haverhill Public Schools in Haverhill, MA.

My Reading Records

Name _____   Month_____

Title / Author	Pages read	Read to myself	Shared with a friend	Shared with my teacher

My favorite book this month was:

Here's a description or picture of the best part:

Library Bookmark

Fill this out when you check out your book:

Title:

Author:

Illustrator:

Date:

I chose this book because:

Name _____

Room Number _____ Grade _____

Students and Parents: This bookmark helps us see how students use the library. Students will receive credit for each bookmark as part of their library grade.

Library Bookmark — Part 2

Fill this out when you are ready to return your book:

Did you read the whole book?

Who helped you to read the book?

What was your opinion?

Loved it! _____

Very good _____

Okay _____

Not too good _____

Hated it! _____

What did you learn from reading this book?

Library Bookmark — Part 3

After you've read your book you might want to share it with the other students in you class or in our school.

Here are some ideas:

Make a book card.

Draw a picture of your favorite part.

Prepare a book talk.

Plan a skit or play.

Design a book jacket.

Tell a friend about the book.

Write to the author.

Make a poster or art display.

Write your own book.

Write a newspaper review.

Design an advertisement.

Design a book jacket.

Read the book to others.

Read another book.

Write music for the story.

Make a tape for listening.

Tell about it during sharing.

Write about it in your journal.

Read it again.

Reading Log

Name _____

Date	Title	Author	# of Pages	Where Read		Read Before		Genre	Level			Complt.		Liked	
				H	S	Y	N		E	M	H	Y	N	Y	N

Reading Contract

WHO?

Developing readers, K–3.

WHY?

Wendy Hood invites her kindergarten students to choose their own books, but like all effective teachers, she needs some way to keep track of their choices. **Reading Contract** enables Wendy and her students to keep track of the books they read as well as how they choose to explore the books.

HOW?

Wendy explains the form to her students the first week of school, and they complete several together as a whole class. After that, she meets briefly with each student, and together they complete the form for each new book chosen. Children are encouraged to record their daily reading by drawing, "This is the way I feel about my reading today."

WHAT ELSE?

Children learn the importance of choosing a book and of monitoring their own reading. By the end of the school year, some children are able to complete the form on their own. The forms are saved in a reading folder and provide a wonderful record of the child's developing reading history.

See: MONITORING p. 24

Reading Contract was developed by Wendy Hood, a primary teacher at Warren Elementary School in Tucson, AZ.

Reading Contract

Name _____ Date _____

Title of the book I am going to read. _____

_____

The number of pages in the book I am going to read. _____

How many days I think it will take me to read this book. _____

I talked with _____ about the book I chose. This is what s/he said:

This is the way I feel about the way I read today:

M	T	W	Th	F

This is what I am going to do to share this book with other kids:

I talked with _____ when I finished the book. This is what we talked about:

Home and School Independent Reading, K–5

WHO?

All elementary students. Similar forms could be developed for middle school and secondary students as well.

WHY?

A wide range of reading fosters learning, perhaps more than any other single experience; therefore, many whole language teachers ask that their students read twenty minutes or more every night at home.

HOW?

The **Home and School Independent Reading** forms (**Grades K–1**, **Grades 2–3**, and **Grades 4–5**), developed by the PAUSD Language Arts Committee, help both parents and students monitor the home reading experience and encourage discussion around every book read.

WHAT ELSE?

Bowing to parental or administrative pressure, many teachers feel compelled to assign nightly homework. It is not always easy to create homework that's truly worthwhile and not just busy work. Requiring students to read at home, on the other hand, is always worthwhile. Reading fosters the intellect, nurtures the emotions, and stirs the imagination while satisfying concerned parents' and administrators' need for homework.

See: REPORTING p. 231

Home and School Independent Reading, K–5, was developed by the Language Arts Committee for Palo Alto Unified School District in Palo Alto, CA, comprising Marianne Jones, Wendla Dyer, Rena Malkofsky, Carolyn Rickard, and Principal Julie Ryan.

Home and School Independent Reading/Grades K–1

Name _____

Grade _____

Title of Book	Date	Did you like the book?		Read with?
		Yes	No	

Home and School Independent Reading/Grades 2–3

Name _____

Grade _____

Title of Book	Date Finished	This book was about (fiction or non-fiction)	Read with?

Home and School Independent Reading/Grades 4–5

Name _____

Grade _____

Title of Book	Date Started	Date Finished	Genre of Book	Comments

Children Learn to Read by Reading

WHO? _____

All developing readers, K–3, and their parents.

WHY? _____

Cindy Elliott developed **Children Learn to Read by Reading** to use with her primary readers as a way to encourage them to read at home with their parents. She also wants parents to understand that the only way children learn to read is by reading—extensively and intensively—and that happens best when parents are involved.

HOW? _____

At the beginning of the year, Cindy sends this letter home together with the form:

Dear Parents,

I would like to ask your help in documenting the reading your child does at home. Please complete the reading form, writing the title of the book your child reads, the date, and your signature. Return the form daily, as this is part of your child's homework. Children learn to read by reading!

Many of the children are emerging as readers. They are just beginning to make sense of print. Using predictable books such as It Looked Like Split Milk *and* The Jigaree *help children predict the text, giving them support as they begin reading.*

If your child has some difficulty, be supportive in helping. Don't get frustrated and frustrate your child. Reading should be fun. Reading is developmental. Just as it took time for your child to learn to talk, it will take time to learn to read. As partners in education, we need to be supportive, allowing our children to make many approximations of the text; we need to encourage our children to be risk-takers, we need to listen to our children read, and we need to be role models by reading ourselves.

With your help and support, I'm confident your child will learn to read, and, just as important, I'm confident your child will enjoy reading. Thank you for your help as a partner in educating your child.

Sincerely,
Mrs. Elliott

WHAT ELSE? _____

Cindy reports that parents' response has been very positive. And children are much more likely to read at home when their parents are involved, keeping track of their reading with the aid of a form.

See: MONITORING p. 18

Children Learn to Read by Reading was developed by Cynthia B. Elliott, a Reading Recovery Teacher Leader for East Baton Rouge Parish Schools, Baton Rouge, LA.

Children Learn to Read by Reading

Name _____

Date	Title of Book	Parent's Signature

Writing Process Overview

WHO?

Haverhill Public School District has developed standardized writing folders for all district students, K–8. With some adaptation for primary students, this form serves to guide and inform the writing process of all students.

WHY?

Although Haverhill Public Schools have had a districtwide writing program in place for more than two years, teachers have found it helpful to remind their students of the writing process at the beginning of each school year. The **Writing Process Overview** reminds students of the steps most writers take in bringing a piece of writing to a final, polished draft.

HOW?

The form is handed out at the beginning of the year. Teachers review the form with their students, making them aware of the steps most writers take as they work to refine and elaborate their meaning in writing.

WHAT ELSE?

Students could keep an overview form with each piece they write, using the form to keep track of and self-evaluate their progress through each phase of the writing process. In this way, both the teacher and student will have a complete record of the evolution of each written composition. In Haverhill Public School District, teachers encourage their students to keep all forms and their computer disks in the left-hand pocket of their folders; they store their drafts in progress and finished pieces in the right-hand pocket until each marking period. At that time, students select their best pieces to be graded.

See: MONITORING pp. 28, 30, 32; INTERACTING pp. 121, 123

*Writing Process Overview was developed by Maureen White, K–8
writing coordinator for Haverhill Public Schools in Haverhill, MA.*

Writing Process Overview

Name _____   Date _____

Title _____

1. Pre-write
   Thinking
   Interviewing
   Listening to a story
   Semantic map (webbing)
   Brainstorming

2. Discovery draft

3. Read your piece to yourself

4. Self-edit to make sense

5. Conference (teacher or peer)

6. Revise your piece using the suggestions you received

7. Proofread your piece to prepare for teacher evaluation or a peer editor if you plan to publish

My Ideas for Writing

WHO?

With some adaptation for primary students, this form will help all students keep track of their writing topics.

WHY?

After a topic launch in which students generate ideas they might be interested in exploring further through writing, students are responsible for keeping a running list of possible writing topics. A form such as this, stapled inside the writing folder, reminds students to record their ideas as they think of them.

HOW?

The **My Ideas for Writing** form is handed out at the beginning of the year. Teachers involve the whole class in a topic launch, which may take place in a variety of ways: the class can brainstorm possible writing topics together, tell stories about real experiences that could become the stuff of writing, bring in meaningful artifacts that tell a story, interview each other, or generate lists of questions they'd like to answer. Students continue to add to the writing idea list all year long and refer to it every time they need to start a new piece.

WHAT ELSE?

Some teachers encourage their students to share their lists with each other and to discuss what ideas they have and how they thought of them. In this way, students inspire and learn from each other. They discover what the writing options are, and more often than not one student's thoughts will trigger ideas for another student.

See: MONITORING pp. 26, 30, 32; INTERACTING pp. 121, 123

My Ideas for Writing was developed by Maureen White, K–8 writing coordinator for Haverhill Public Schools in Haverhill, MA.

My Ideas for Writing

Name _____   Grade _____

Topic   Date   Topic   Date

_____   _____

_____   _____

_____   _____

_____   _____

_____   _____

_____   _____

_____   _____

_____   _____

_____   _____

_____   _____

_____   _____

_____   _____

_____   _____

_____   _____

_____   _____

_____   _____

_____   _____

_____   _____

_____   _____

_____   _____

Writing Workshop: Status of the Class

WHO?

This form helps teachers of all grade levels to keep track of the writing their students are doing.

WHY?

Originally developed by Nancie Atwell (1987), the **Writing Workshop: Status of the Class** form enables teachers to quickly check in with every student at the beginning of writer's workshop. In this way, teachers can ascertain where every student is in the writing process. The quick check-in helps students to consider and identify how they are going to spend their workshop time, and, as they listen to their peers talk about what they are going to do, it expands the range of writing options for all students.

HOW?

Many teachers find it most convenient to keep this form on a clipboard. At the beginning of writing workshop, they gather in a circle with their students. While each student takes a few seconds to identify what they are going to be doing during the workshop, the teacher jots it down. Students then return to their seats with a clear plan of how they are going to spend their workshop time.

WHAT ELSE?

At a glance, the form helps teachers identify what students are doing, who is making satisfactory progress, and who is not. In this way, teachers can quickly tell if a student needs encouragement, instructional support, or some focused nudging.

Reference

Atwell, N. 1987. *In the middle: Writing, reading, and learning with adolescents*. Montclair, NJ: Boynton/Cook.

See: MONITORING pp. 26, 28, 32; INTERACTING pp. 121, 123

Writing Workshop: Status of the Class was developed by Maureen White, K–8 writing coordinator for Haverhill Public Schools in Haverhill, MA.

Writing Workshop: Status of the Class

Name _____   Grade _____

Legend: 1. New text   3. Conferencing   5. Revising
          2. Working on draft   4. Computing   6. Editing

Names Date																			
1																			
2																			
3																			
4																			
5																			
6																			
7																			
8																			
9																			
10																			
11																			
12																			
13																			
14																			
15																			
16																			
17																			
18																			
19																			
20																			
21																			
22																			
23																			
24																			
25																			
26																			
27																			
28																			
29																			
30																			
31																			
32																			
33																			
34																			
35																			

Writing Record · Writing Workshop Report

WHO?

With some adaptation for primary students, these forms will work for all grade levels. The **Writing Workshop Report** was designed for teachers; **Writing Record** is for students to complete.

WHY?

In writer's workshop, all students work at their own pace on topics of their own choosing. Detailed record keeping is essential for a successful workshop. Encouraging students to keep track of their writing in this way not only helps them monitor and document their progress, but serves to inform the teacher as he or she works to keep abreast of the writing developments for thirty-some students.

HOW?

Students keep Writing Record inside their writing folder. They record the title of every piece they are working on, the dates of each completed draft, and the date they finish. In addition, using the form encourages them to consider their revision strategies and writing goals.

WHAT ELSE?

At a glance, the forms help teachers identify what students are doing, who is making satisfactory progress, and who is not. In this way, teachers can quickly tell if a student needs encouragement, instructional support, or some focused nudging.

See: MONITORING pp. 28, 30; INTERACTING pp. 121, 123

Writing Record was developed by Palo Alto Unified School District.

Writing Workshop Report was developed by Karen Sabers Dalrymple, who works for Ashland Public Schools in Ashland, OR.

Writing Record

Name _____ Date _____ Grade _____

Titles of Writings in Progress	How Far I Took this Piece			My Comments
	Draft	Revised	Published	

Writing Workshop Report

Teacher _____   Grade/Year _____   Student _____

Type of Writing	Quarter 1		Quarter 2		Quarter 3		Quarter 4	
	No. of Pieces	No. Publish	No. of Pieces	No. Publish	No. of Pieces	No. Publish	No. of Pieces	No. Publish
Personal Narrative								
Poetry								
Fiction								
Nonfiction								

Comments:

Spelling Discovery

WHO?

All elementary students; the form may also be appropriate for middle school and secondary students.

WHY?

Teachers who encourage children to actively explore the orthographic system know that sometimes, just by attending to and experimenting with alternate spellings, children will discover the conventional spelling. In addition, the **Spelling Discovery** form provides both students and teacher with a record of the words each student is learning to spell.

HOW?

Avery Walker's students keep this form stapled inside their writing folders. When it's time to edit their compositions, they underline the words they think are misspelled, then attempt to spell the words correctly by themselves. They can also ask a friend for spelling assistance, check a dictionary, or discover the conventional spelling in some other way. In the process, students become aware of the range of efficient spelling strategies that they can use.

WHAT ELSE?

We've all seen students who score 100% on the Friday morning spelling test and then turn around and misspell the very words they got right on the test. That's because students don't learn to spell by memorizing lists of isolated words. But most teachers feel the need to address spelling in some way. A simple list such as Spelling Discovery can fulfill that need. To make it an even more effective tool, invite students to notice and keep track of any patterns they might discover in their spelling miscues. Sandra Wilde's book, *You Kan Red This!* contains many helpful suggestions for charting the patterns of children's spelling miscues. Once teachers gain insight into their students' orthographic logic, they can determine how best to nudge them toward conventional spelling.

Reference

Wilde, S. 1991. *You kan red this!* Portsmouth, NH: Heinemann.

See: ANALYZING p. 143

Spelling Discovery was developed by Avery D. Walker, a first/second-grade teacher at Ohlone School in Palo Alto, CA.

Spelling Discovery

Name _____   Date _____   Grade _____

My Try

With Help from a Friend, Dictionary, Other

My Plans · Center Committee Plans

WHO?

Debra Goodman developed these forms for her fifth-grade students. Accordingly, the form reflects her curriculum and instructional strategies. Teachers of any grade level can create similar forms that reflect their classroom learning experiences and that achieve a similar purpose: helping students keep track of their learning.

WHY?

The most effective learners are often those who can direct, monitor, and document their own learning. Simple forms like **My Plans** help students understand what the options are while providing them with some choice and ownership over their own learning. At the same time, the form helps students keep track of work in progress as well as its successful completion. Student and teacher record keeping is essential when students have a great deal of choice in learning experiences.

HOW?

Debra Goodman writes: "A certain amount of trust is necessary as students record their own work. Learning to keep good records takes time. Initially, I take some class time to have students fill out their **My Plans** record sheets following time spent in centers, reading, writing, etc. As students learn to work independently and record their own work, I can review record sheets quickly and pull those that look spotty. In a work conference, I can discover whether work isn't getting done or records aren't being kept. During the first parent conference, for example, I invariably discover that a child who is not turning in completed forms is an avid reader who is not keeping good records."

Debra also invites her students to work in committees to plan center experiences for their peers. The **Center Committee Plans** form helps them plan and organize their ideas, and enables her to support their ideas by providing additional resources as needed.

WHAT ELSE?

Based on a review of the daily forms, and with teacher assistance, students might write up a learning plan in which they outline for themselves how to revise their work strategies to make more productive use of their classroom learning time. Debra explains: "While I don't equate learning with good records, I do push students to keep good records of their learning experiences. This ongoing self-evaluation helps students learn to recognize and share with others their own strengths, abilities, and achievements. They can see the immediate value of the process, since it enables them to get credit for a variety of learning experiences, both at school and at home."

See: MONITORING p. 40

My Plans and Center Committee Plans were developed by Debra Goodman, who teaches fifth grade at the Dewey Learning Center in Detroit, MI.

My Plans

Name _____   Week of _____

MAKE-UP WORK

1. Quiet Work Center (Sports)
- ____ a. Listen to a story or author tape
- ____ b. Work on your portfolio
- ____ c. Map activity or map puzzle
- ____ d. Wherezit
- ____ e. Jigsaw puzzle
- ____ f. Research: your choice

2. Post Office/Writing Center
- ____ a. Write a letter
- ____ b. Write with a story starter
- ____ c. Writing: your choice

3. Library
- ____ a. Choose a book to read
- ____ b. Read one of our favorite author books
- ____ c. Work on a reading response
- ____ d. Meet with your literature group
- ____ e. Reading: your choice

4. Science Center
- ____ a. Make an observation of your plant
- ____ b. Science activity (with activity sheet)
- ____ c. Read a science book or magazine
- ____ d. Write or draw about science topic
- ____ e. Science: your choice

5. Math Center
- ____ a. Meet with your math group
- ____ b. Fraction Bars game (record your results)
- ____ c. Design block activity
- ____ d. Math puzzler
- ____ e. Geo-board worksheet
- ____ f. Cuisenaire rods activity
- ____ g. Math: your choice

6. Work Center
- ____ a. Writing
- ____ b. Reading response
- ____ c. Math
- ____ d. Ranger Rick's
- ____ e. Journal
- ____ f. Science
- ____ g. Work: your choice

7. Free Choice (completed two work choices for day)
- ____ a. Draw
- ____ b. Chess
- ____ c. Legos
- ____ d. Checkers
- ____ e. Knitting
- ____ f. Book illustration
- ____ g. Your choice

	Monday	Tuesday	Wednesday	Thursday	Friday
Reading	_____	_____	_____	_____	_____
Journal	_____	_____	_____	_____	_____
Work 1	_____	_____	_____	_____	_____
Work 2	_____	_____	_____	_____	_____
Free Choice	_____	_____	_____	_____	_____

Center Committee Plans

Name _____ Date _____ Grade _____

Center Committee plans for _____

Committee members _____

What learning experience are you planning for next week?

What will students learn from this activity?

What materials will you need?

What will you need to do to prepare the center for this activity?

What other choices will students have at your center this week?

Who will help students with the activity?

Monday: Tuesday: Wednesday: Thursday: Friday:

Will you need an adult to help with anything?

Research Contract ·
Showing You Know

WHO?

All students.

WHY?

Whole language teachers invite their students to engage in real research. Students are encouraged to ask and explore their own questions about the world—topics in which they have a personal interest.

HOW?

Forms such as **Research Contract** support students as independent researchers and guide them through the inquiry process. To find answers to their questions, students use a variety of resources and research tools such as surveys, interviews with experts, fiction and nonfiction books, magazines, newspapers, and artifacts. When they have collected, collated, and made sense of their data, students then present their findings to their peers. Their presentations may take a variety of formats: slide shows, poster sessions, charts and diagrams, scientific demonstrations, and dramatic performances. In this way, children come to understand that learning begins with asking questions and following a line of inquiry. They also learn that information is available from a variety of sources; in fact, the best source is often another person. Finally, as they share and explain their research project to others, they learn that teaching is often the best way to learn.

WHAT ELSE?

We bring the learning cycle full circle when we invite our students to share with a real audience what they have learned. Learning how to transfer information from one format to another as students represent their learning to themselves and to others is invaluable, as is the process they engage in as they determine which format is appropriate for their data and findings. **Showing You Know** lists many different ways to present information. Almost all the presentational formats can be adapted to various grade levels.

See: MONITORING pp. 37, 43

Research Contract was developed by an unknown third-grade class.
Showing You Know was developed by Lois Bridges Bird.

Research Contract

I, _____ am anxious to do research on (topic, ideas, etc.)

_____

_____

My plan of study will be _____

_____

_____

I will use the following resources _____

_____

_____

The date I will start is _____

I will present a progress report on _____

and conclude my study on _____

I shall present my activity in the form of

    ☐ Class presentation

    ☐ Play

    ☐ Report

    ☐ Other _____

_____

I understand that I am able to negotiate a new contract at the time of my progress report if need be.

_____ _____ _____ _____
Signed   Dated   Witness   Dated

Showing You Know

- **Letters to the Editor**
  If you have some new information or have developed a unique perspective on a particular issue that you would like to share with the public, consider writing to the editor of your local newspaper or to the editor of an appropriate magazine or journal. Explain what you did and what you found and why you have assumed your particular stance.

- **Poster Sessions, Bulletin Board**
  Create a poster or bulletin board display with headlines and caption, charts, diagrams, and so on, and explain it to the class. Be prepared to answer questions.

- **Scrapbook or Photo Album**
  Arrange your notes, pictures, graphs, or articles in a scrapbook or photo album and write a description of your research process and findings.

- **Oral Histories and Interviews**
  In keeping with the Foxfire tradition, transcribe tapes from your interviews and present them with photographs, artwork, artifacts, and background information.

- **Newspaper**
  Do an edition that is related to a historical time period—every article, editorial, advertisement, and so on should reflect the time period you studied.

- **Surveys, Interviews, Questionnaires**
  Design tools for collecting further information.

- **Slide or Video Presentation**
  Represent your findings through a video or slide presentation. Write an accompanying script.

- **Debate or Panel Discussion**
  If you worked with a partner or as a part of a group, and you reached different conclusions, present and debate your different positions. Or present your findings as a panel; be prepared to field questions from the audience. One member should serve as the moderator.

- **Models and Maps**
  Lifesize or to scale, cross-sections, dioramas, shadow boxes, mobiles; relief; trace routes on road maps.

- **Diagrams, Tables, Graphs, Flowcharts, Timelines**
  Chart the sequential steps involved in making something—if you conducted an experiment, the steps you followed; or represent the chronology of a historical event you studied. You can also capture this information in a how-to book written so someone else can follow your procedure.

- **Role-Playing, Socio-Drama**
  Role-playing is an effective way to present a biography; try socio-drama for a dramatic resentation of a historical or current sociopolitical event.

- **Folk Art, Songs and Dances, Food**
  Present and describe folk art from the time period or region you studied; or perform representational songs and dances; or give us a taste of your project and prepare regional or ethnic food; prepare enough for all to sample! Include recipes.

- **Museum Kits**
  Create an attractive display of objects that represents your topic and provide written explanations.

Planning Grid for Thematic Study

WHO?

The planning grid works across all grade levels.

WHY?

Debra Goodman explains how she uses the planning grid:"In my classroom, evaluation doesn't come *after* the learning experience. Evaluation is a process woven into every aspect of the learning experience. I usually plan my evaluation strategies at the same time that I plan the learning experiences. I brainstorm all of the concepts and experiences I want to get across, and then organize them on the **Planning Grid for Thematic Study** and also into a timeline. This helps me to make sure that I keep my energy focused and see the project through to the end. I have learned to plan evaluation strategies right away, which helps me to pay attention to the learning process rather than focus only on final projects.

HOW?

"My students and I plan together. We select our theme topic or topics and discuss what we already know. I often bring in artifacts, books, films, or pictures to help us start to focus on the topic. We brainstorm questions about things that we want to know and brainstorm possible learning experiences. With the students' ideas in mind, I can sit down alone (or with a planning team) and use the planning grid to begin to map out the experiences, the classroom set-up, and the timeline for thematic study." (A completed planning grid appears on the next page as a model for teachers to use in filling out their own forms.)

WHAT ELSE?

"In the course of a thematic unit and throughout the school year, I use these evaluation strategies:
- *Record keeping*—using checklists, planning sheets, or evaluation sheets for student and teacher to keep track of learning experiences.
- *Written documents*—such as journals, notes, webs, charts, and other evidence of student learning.
- *Observation and conferences*—throughout the learning process, to observe students' understandings, strategies, questions, and abilities.
- *Sampling*—taking an in-depth look at the learning process through a piece of work.
- *Presentations*—demonstrating learning through teaching others.
- *Self-evaluations*—of progress or entire-theme study, which ask students to consider what they have learned from the theme study.
- *Evaluation with parents*—using a variety of formats such as self-evaluations, checklists, and narrative reports."

See: MONITORING pp. 37, 40

Planning Grid for Thematic Study was developed by Debra Goodman, who teaches fifth grade at the Dewey Learning Center in Detroit, MI.

Planning Grid for Thematic Study

Name _____ Date _____ Grade _____

	Whole Class	Small Group	Independent
CONCEPTS	What is culture? Native Americans Immigrants: (cultural background, historic trends, why different groups came to the U.S.) What is custom, language? What cultural groups are represented in our classroom?	Specific cultural study Specific customs	Family history Own family immigrants Customs of families Culture of my family
STRATEGIES/ PROCESSES	Brainstorm, web Ask questions Conduct interviews Note-taking mini-lesson Organize information (mapping, outlining) Use consensus Share different media	Work in committee Talk and listen Interview, read Share notes, organize Editing in committees Group conferences Reading partners, circles Use consensus	Organize for research Compose questions Interview, read Take notes Reflective logs Confer Organize Present information
LEARNING EXPERIENCES	Group discussions Shared readings Movies Folk songs and ballads Folk dance Simulations of events Library, museum visits Presentations	Cultural studies Literature circles Group skits, songs Writing groups Discussions Plan presentations	Family histories Independent reading Listen (records, tapes) Independent research Class museum Family artifacts (cultural artifacts)

(continued)

Planning Grid for Thematic Study

	Whole Class	Small Group	Independent
MATERIALS	(A list of specific resources in these areas): Human resources and community agencies Literature Music, art, and dance Others:	Nonfiction (for read-aloud, research, and literature circles) Fiction (for read-aloud, research, and literature circles) Poetry, songs, and other forms for sharing and participation Listening post (folk records and tapes, historic tapes) Class museum (family and cultural artifacts) Library (book collection and displays) Writing (reference materials, writing materials) Art (materials for folk crafts)	
EVALUATION	Literature response log Sharing of new information Family history presentations Group webbing and webbing of shared knowledge Individual conference Class display day Class questions (oral and written)	Group reporting of progress Group projects and reports Peer conferences	Committee discussions Unit work records Family project Group evaluations Sharing Self-evaluation Writing folder

Planning Grid for Thematic Study

Name _____   Date _____   Grade _____

	Whole Class	Small Group	Independent
CONCEPTS			
STRATEGIES/ PROCESSES			
LEARNING EXPERIENCES			

(continued)

	Whole Class	Small Group	Independent
MATERIALS			

EVALUATION

Observing: What's Going On?

Kidwatching Guidelines

WHO? _____

These guidelines will help teachers of all grade levels engage in sensitive and thoughtful observation of their students.

WHY? _____

You can gather valuable information about your students as learners by standing on the sidelines and observing and listening to them in a variety of social and instructional settings. **Kidwatching Guidelines** offers suggestions for effective observation.

HOW? _____

You may choose to observe one student working alone, a student as a member of a group, all members of a small group, or the class as a whole. You may record your general impressions or use observation to confirm or reject specific notions regarding the students. Some teachers find setting aside a specific period of time daily for systematic observation of individual students is the most effective way to handle this strategy; others keep a clipboard on hand for continuous note-taking as they see things happening that are worth recording. Still others prefer to record their notes on post-its or mailing labels. These can be peeled off and placed inside a student's manila folder for safe-keeping.

WHAT ELSE? _____

In the rush of classroom activity, it is rarely possible to reflect on and interpret the significance of kidwatching data. While they are with their students during class time, many experienced kid-watchers simply jot down a few key words that serve to jog their memories later when they return to their notes during lunch or after school. Away from the fast pace of classroom life, teachers can take the time to think about the meaning of what they observed and how they might use it to plan sensitive instruction and create supportive curriculum.

Debra Goodman keeps her anecdotal notebook open and available to her students. When she sees something significant (a student's learning breakthrough, for example), she asks the student to record the event in her notebook. In this way, students not only recognize the significance of their own learning, but they have the opportunity to write about it, reflect on it, and to extend and refine the meaning of the experience.

See: OBSERVING p. 57

Kidwatching Guidelines were developed by Yetta M. Goodman, professor of Reading, Language, and Culture at the School of Education, University of Arizona, Tucson.

Kidwatching Guidelines

1. Know what, how, and when to observe.

2. Know how language and learning operate.

3. Observe in a variety of social-cultural settings. What is the student reading on the street? at home? in the library? Relate to the student's interests.

4. Observe reading by watching and listening to kids read familiar material. Base evaluation on what the child knows about reading.

5. Observe writing by watching kids write. Base evaluation on what the child knows about writing.

6. Explore the nature of miscues—miscues are indicators of all language development.

   a. Everyone makes miscues and has misconceptions.

   b. Miscues reveal interpretative differences.

   c. Miscues reveal the revision and editing processes.

   d. Focus on high-level miscues that indicate reading effectiveness and efficiency.

7. Understand responses in relation to the social/cultural view of the learner.

8. View "right" answers with care.

9. Ask "Why is this happening? What does this tell me about the intellectual functioning of the learner?"

Complete Anecdotal Form · Anecdotal Observation Sheet

WHO?

Appropriate for all whole language teachers and students.

WHY?

Helps teachers systematically monitor and document their students' learning. Records of such kidwatching data informs teachers, helping them plan sensitive instruction and create supportive, stimulating curriculum.

HOW?

Carlen Luke admits that before she developed the **Complete Anecdotal Form** she wrote her observations of her students on the "margin of the class list or back of the weekly bulletin." The notes she managed not to lose gave her an incomplete picture of each student. Now she successfully uses the form, which takes up the back and front of one page. She has one for each child, and keeps them in a binder on her desk. The form has eight categories: reading, writing, oral language, research, math, family/self/social behavior, parent contact, and other.

Carlen explains how she uses the form: "The only time during class that I write in the binder is when a child is reading to me. I take notes about the strategies the child is using, how well the child understands the passage, and what my recommendations are. Every week or two I'll sit down and go through the binder page by page, recalling what I've noticed about each child. I still have some notes scribbled on backs of tardy slips, but now if I find them, I know exactly what to do with them."

The **Anecdotal Observation Sheet** asks the observer to focus on four learning strategies: question posing, risk-taking, collaboration and cooperation, and sharing knowledge.

WHAT ELSE?

Carlen uses her anecdotal records to help with report cards. First, she reads through the binder to see which kids she needs to observe more in which areas. Then, every quarter she reads through everything she's written about each student and writes a summary statement for each student across each of her eight observational focuses. She staples her summaries to the students' report cards, giving parents a much fuller picture of their child's progress than rows of grades could ever do.

See: OBSERVING pp. 47, 53, 55, 57

Complete Anecdotal Form was developed by Carlen Luke, teacher of a third/fourth-grade combination class at Fair Oaks School in Redwood City, CA.

Anecdotal Observation Sheet was developed by Diana Mazzuchi, Nancy Brooks, and Maggie Shine, who teach a multi-grade 1,2,3 class in Brattleboro, VT.

Complete Anecdotal Form

Name _____   Date _____   Grade _____

Reading	Writing	Oral Language

Research

(continued)

Math	Family/Self/Social Behavior	Parent Contact

Other

Anecdotal Observation Sheet

Group _____

Grade _____

Names	Question Posing	Risk-Taking	Collaboration & Cooperation	Sharing Knowledge

Anecdotal Records

WHO?

Primary, elementary, and secondary students

WHY?

In her busy and fast-paced kindergarten class, Katherine Der Mugrdechian knows a lot intuitively about her thirty-one students. Still, she wanted to keep written records of her observations but needed to find a simple yet efficient method to authentically note and assess what each child was doing in multiple curricular areas.

HOW?

Katherine explains: "My students have an **Anecdotal Records** sheet that is stored in their language arts folder. The sheet is divided into six areas: Reading, Writing, Math, Oral Language, Inside Play, and Outside Play. These can be changed to other focuses in other years or additional focuses can be added on the reverse side.

"Using copier labels (or address labels for dry-toner office copiers), I type the names in the master spacer and run the copier label sheets in place of paper. Each child's name is on the one sheet, which has room for thirty-two names. With the sheet of labels on a clipboard it becomes very easy to target an area for observation and write down my comments for each child, as well as to know which children remain to be observed. Once all the children have been observed for a specific area, I date the labels and place them in the correct space on the Anecdotal Records sheet in their Language Arts Folder."

WHAT ELSE?

As the school year progresses and a child's Anecdotal Records sheet is filled with anecdotal labels, it is possible to get a clear picture of the child's development. The record sheet provides a holistic view of the child and what he or she has done throughout the year.

See: OBSERVING pp. 47, 49, 55, 57

Anecdotal Records was developed by Katherine Der Mugrdechian, who teaches kindergarten at Burroughs Elementary School in Fresno, CA.

Anecdotal Records

Name _____ Date _____ Grade _____

Reading

Writing

Math

Oral Language

Inside Play

Outside Play

Parent Observation

WHO?

Primary students.

WHY?

Diana Mazzuchi, Nancy Brooks, and Maggie Shine have developed a "process curriculum" in which they engage their students in cooperative groups to research something of their choice.

HOW?

Each year they have a broad theme under which students choose topics to research. Students work together in small, collaborative research groups. As often as possible, their research leads them outside the classroom on field trips. Parents accompany them and take responsibility for leading the small groups. As part of their participation as group leaders, parents complete a **Parent Observation** form that captures the interaction of the children in their groups. In this way, the teachers have a record of each small group's response to the field trip experience.

WHAT ELSE?

As parents complete this form, they develop a new awareness of and appreciation for the sorts of language—questions and comments—that reflect learning. This, in turn, enhances their interactions with their own children.

See: OBSERVING pp. 47, 49, 53

Parent Observation was developed by Diana Mazzuchi, Nancy Brooks, and Maggie Shine, who teach a multi-grade 1,2,3 class in Brattleboro, VT.

Parent Observation

Parent Name _____   Date _____

Trip to _____

Student Name				
Questions Children Asked				
Comments Children Made				
Seemed Focused?	☐ Yes ☐ No	☐ Yes ☐ No	☐ Yes ☐ No	☐ Yes ☐ No
Listened?	☐ Yes ☐ No	☐ Yes ☐ No	☐ Yes ☐ No	☐ Yes ☐ No
Comments				

Whole Language Checklist

WHO?

This form would work well for students in second grade through eighth; with some adaptation, it could serve younger and older students as well.

WHY?

Caryl Crowell explains: "Having been encouraged as a kidwatcher by Yetta Goodman and others, I began keeping a list of learning behaviors that I observed in my students and considered to be signs of their growth, especially in terms of literacy. Compiled with the results of miscue analyses and writing samples, they presented a fairly complete view of the children as literacy users within the context of a classroom. As I expanded my professional knowledge about evaluation in whole language classrooms and about the development of literacy in children, my list began to reflect not only the behaviors I observed in my students, but the ones I hoped to see. In other words, the list was a statement of my goals for the class as well as a record of what was already occurring.

HOW?

"The **Whole Language Checklist** is updated and sent home quarterly to enable parents to see how their child's literacy is developing. I deliberately leave lots of room for comments on the checklist and encourage parents to make use of this space to let me know about important literacy events at home. Not too many parents over the years have made use of the comment space, but those who did have mentioned how much it meant to them to have their own views of their children as learners valued by their child's teacher.

WHAT ELSE?

"I have used the checklist now for four years and it has changed yearly. Every class has been different and I have found a need to adapt the checklist to express the interests and abilities of each group. Also, as I have grown as a teacher, the checklist has accommodated my expanding knowledge of first- and second-language literacy acquisition, my evolving theoretical framework, and my changing view of children as they continue to surprise me with their sophistication as learners."

See: OBSERVING pp. 47, 74

Whole Language Checklist was developed by Caryl G. Crowell, a bilingual teacher at Borton Primary Magnet School in Tucson, AZ.

Whole Language Checklist

Name _____   Date _____   Grade _____

Native language _____   Second language _____

Evaluation code: 1 - rarely observed
                    2 - sometimes observed
                    3 - often observed

ORAL LANGUAGE DEVELOPMENT	1	2	3	4	COMMENTS
Listens attentively when others speak					
in one-to-one interactions					
in small groups					
in large groups					
to stories read aloud					
Participates and takes turns appropriately in conversations					
Elaborates responses					
Explains thinking					
Talks about language					
Engages in language play					
Demonstrates understanding of oral directions					

LITERACY DEVELOPMENT

• READING

	1	2	3	4	
Selects own reading material					
Initiates reading promptly					
Reads for a sustained period					
Reads a variety of material					
Reads for enjoyment, information, and research					
Uses library resources for enjoyment and research					
Attempts to make meaningful substitutions for unknown words					
Uses language sense and meaning to make and confirm predictions					
Monitors own reading and self-corrects					

(continued)

• LITERATURE RESPONSE	1	2	3	4	COMMENTS
Retells and summarizes stories					
Relates reading to personal experiences					
Demonstrates awareness of story elements: plot, characters, theme, setting, etc.					
Recognizes a variety of genre: fairy tale, folktale, poetry, drama, biography, etc.					
Discusses reading with others					
Extends reading experiences through other related reading and projects					
Writes thoughtfully in literature log					
WRITING					
Self-selects writing topics and ideas					
Engages promptly in and sustains writing activities					
Writes for a variety of purposes and audiences					
Uses a variety of styles, forms, and literary devices					
Ideas/story are developed cohesively and sequentially					
Writing shows character and theme development					
Uses a variety of vocabulary and sentence structures					
Writes in paragraphs with topic sentences and supporting details					
Shares and discusses writing with others					
Revises for clarity and meaning					
Self-edits for conventions					
Uses appropriate resources to support writing process					
WRITING MECHANICS					
Explores uses of punctuation					
Uses end punctuation appropriately					
Uses other punctuation appropriately					
Uses capitals and lower case letters appropriately					
Uses age-appropriate handwriting					

(continued)

SPELLING	1	2	3	4	COMMENTS
Uses invented spelling freely					
Invented spellings are easily read and show appropriate letter-sound correspondences					
High frequency words show standard spelling					
Invented spelling shows awareness of spelling patterns					
Spelling shows visualization of words					
Many words show standard spelling					
MATH PROBLEM SOLVING					
Uses manipulatives effectively					
Uses representational drawings appropriately					
Solves problems at the abstract level					
Attempts to solve problems in an organized way					
Estimates answers. Considers reasonableness of answers					
Discusses problem solving strategies					
Keeps working when answer is not immediately apparent					
Makes mental calculations					
LEARNING IN A SOCIAL ENVIRONMENT					
Is organized and has necessary materials					
Begins work promptly and stays on task to appropriate closure or completion					
Self-directed and self-motivated					
Uses room resources for information and clarification					
Uses other children as resources					
Collaborates effectively with others. Does his or her share					
Values ideas and contributions of others					
Takes risks as a learner					
Interactions show respect for safety and feelings of others					
Assumes responsibility for solving social problems verbally					
Self-evaluates					

(continued)

SECOND-LANGUAGE DEVELOPMENT	1	2	3	4	COMMENTS
Demonstrates interest in learning a second language					
Listens attentively when second language is used					
Attempts purposeful communication in second language					
Builds/draws upon knowledge of native language					
Demonstrates ongoing development of literacy in second language					

GENERAL COMMENTS (to be used by parents and teacher)

1.

2.

3.

4.

Profile of Language Arts Outcomes, K–5

WHO?

Kindergarten through fifth-grade students.

WHY?

Palo Alto Unified School District has listed expected language arts outcomes across grade level in order to give all elementary teachers clear, global guidelines regarding development. PAUSD teachers are encouraged to use these guidelines to monitor and support their students' developing control over both oral and written language.

HOW?

Originally, the **Profile of Language Arts Outcomes** (**Grades K–1**, **Grades 2–3**, and **Grades 4–5**) appeared in the form of a checklist (see *The Whole Language Catalog: Supplement on Authentic Assessment*, 1992, p. 110). But recognizing the recursive, cyclical nature of development, PAUSD teachers decided that a continuum better represented their students' learning. Under each language modality, the global expectations are listed. Then the behavioral indicators of those outcomes are listed along a two-way arrow. Teachers may use the profile in a variety of ways. Some teachers prefer to keep a profile on each student. Others use it as a reference guide as they record narrative information in their anecdotal notebooks.

WHAT ELSE?

It's not surprising that our assessment instruments reflect our evolving understanding of what assessment is, how it impacts instruction and curriculum, and how it guides teachers and students in the learning/teaching process. As Ken Goodman has written, "If we could characterize the nature of educational assessment in a single word in the present period, it would be 'changing.'" What's important is that teachers be fully involved in designing the instruments, administering them, collecting the data, making sense of it all, and revising the instrument as needed.

Reference

Goodman, K. S., Bird, L. B., and Goodman, Y. M. (Eds.). 1992. *The whole language catalog: Supplement on authentic assessment.* Santa Rosa, CA: American School Publishers.

See: OBSERVING p. 84

Profile of Language Arts Outcomes, K–5, was developed by a subcommittee of the Palo Alto Unified School District Language Arts Committee, comprising teachers Marianne Jones, Rena Malkofsky, Carolyn Rickard, Wendla Dyer, and Principal Julie Ryan.

Profile of Language Arts Outcomes/Grades K-1

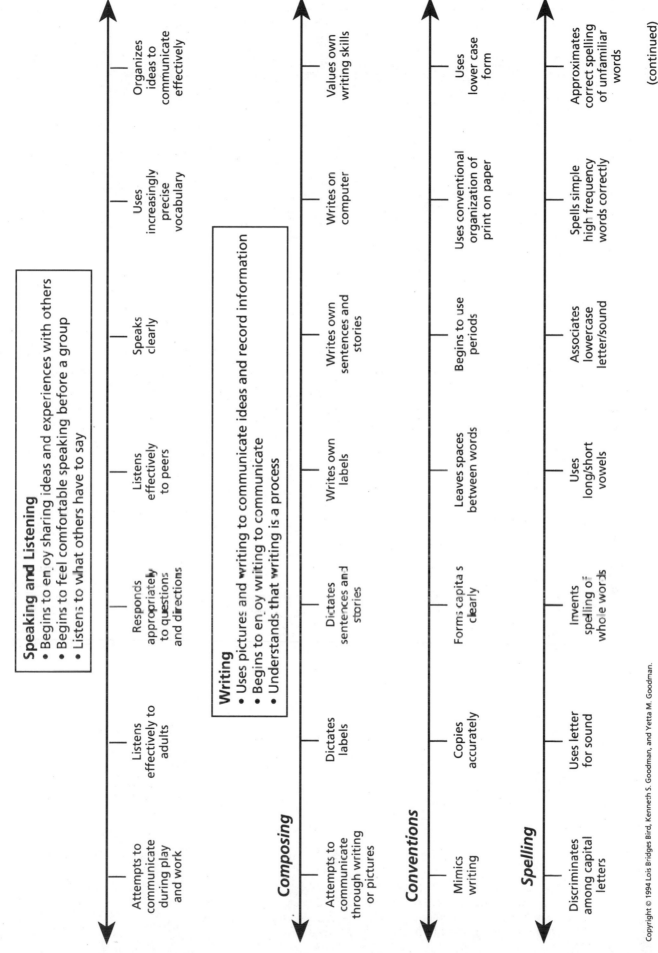

Speaking and Listening
- Begins to enjoy sharing ideas and experiences with others
- Begins to feel comfortable speaking before a group
- Listens to what others have to say

Writing
- Uses pictures and writing to communicate ideas and record information
- Begins to enjoy writing to communicate
- Understands that writing is a process

Listens effectively to adults · Responds appropriately to questions and directions · Listens effectively to peers · Speaks clearly · Uses increasingly precise vocabulary · Organizes ideas to communicate effectively

Attempts to communicate during play and work

Composing

Attempts to communicate through writing or pictures · Dictates labels · Dictates sentences and stories · Writes own labels · Writes own sentences and stories · Writes on computer · Values own writing skills

Conventions

Mimics writing · Copies accurately · Forms capitals clearly · Leaves spaces between words · Begins to use periods · Uses conventional organization of print on paper · Uses lower case form

Spelling

Discriminates among capital letters · Uses letter for sound · Invents spelling of whole words · Uses long/short vowels · Associates lowercase letter/sound · Spells simple high frequency words correctly · Approximates correct spelling of unfamiliar words

(continued)

Profile of Language Arts Outcomes/Grades K-1

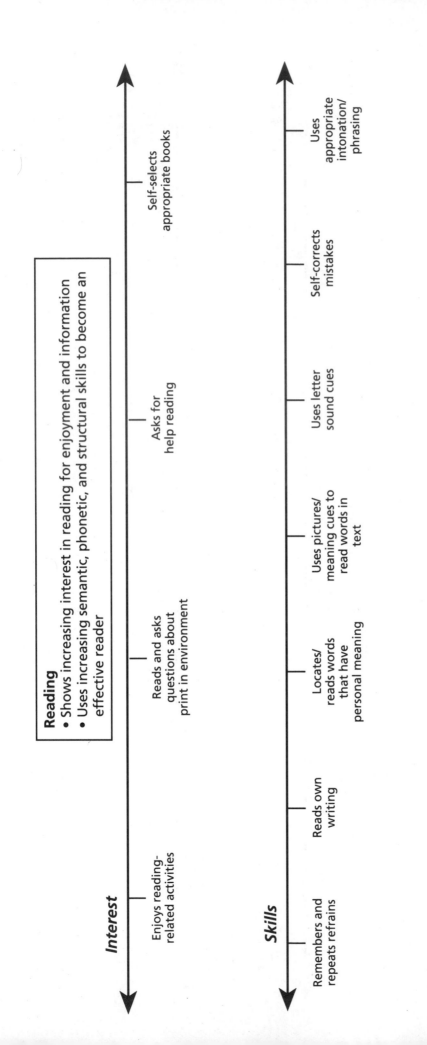

Interest

Enjoys reading-related activities

Reads own writing

Reads and asks questions about print in environment

Asks for help reading

Self-selects appropriate books

Reading
- Shows increasing interest in reading for enjoyment and information
- Uses increasing semantic, phonetic, and structural skills to become an effective reader

Skills

Remembers and repeats refrains

Locates/reads words that have personal meaning

Uses pictures/meaning cues to read words in text

Uses letter sound cues

Self-corrects mistakes

Uses appropriate intonation/phrasing

Profile of Language Arts Outcomes/Grades 2-3

Speaking and Listening
- Enjoys sharing work, ideas, and experiences with others
- Feels comfortable speaking before a group
- Respects what others have to say
- Understands that language is a tool for clarifying thinking and learning, sharing ideas, and resolving conflict

Participates in group poetry activities, dramatization, storytelling

Individually recites simple poems and tells stories

Follows multi-step directions

Participates appropriately in group discussions (takes turns contributes)

Uses increasingly precise and descriptive vocabulary

Asks questions that show higher-order thinking to clarify understanding

Prepares and presents simple oral reports

Learning to use active listening skills (engagement and responsiveness)

Composing

Writing
- Writes for a variety of purposes and audiences
- Perseveres through the writing process: pre-write, draft, respond, revise, edit, share/publish
- Uses literature as a model for writing
- Writes across the curriculum
- Writes with increasing independence and fluency

Engages in pre-writing (discussion, word webs, frames, brainstorming, clustering)

Stays with one topic throughout first draft

Accepts response from adult and sometimes applies feedback to revise content, organization, word choice

Uses increasingly complex vocabulary and sentence structures

Composes in the four writing types:
- narrative
- descriptive
- expository: informative
- expository: analytical

Begins to provide, accept, and apply peer feedback

Values own writing skills

(continued)

Conventions

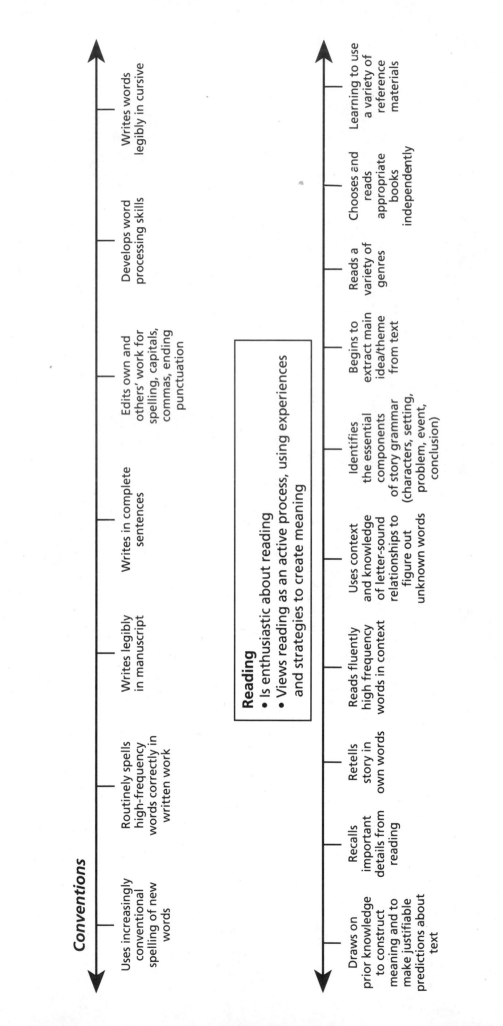

Reading
- Is enthusiastic about reading
- Views reading as an active process, using experiences and strategies to create meaning

Uses increasingly conventional spelling of new words

Routinely spells high-frequency words correctly in written work

Writes legibly in manuscript

Writes in complete sentences

Edits own and others' work for spelling, capitals, commas, ending punctuation

Develops word processing skills

Writes words legibly in cursive

Draws on prior knowledge to construct meaning and to make justifiable predictions about text

Recalls important details from reading

Retells story in own words

Reads fluently high frequency words in context

Uses context and knowledge of letter-sound relationships to figure out unknown words

Identifies the essential components of story grammar (characters, setting, problem, event, conclusion)

Begins to extract main idea/theme from text

Reads a variety of genres

Chooses and reads appropriate books independently

Learning to use a variety of reference materials

Profile of Language Arts Outcomes/Grades 4-5

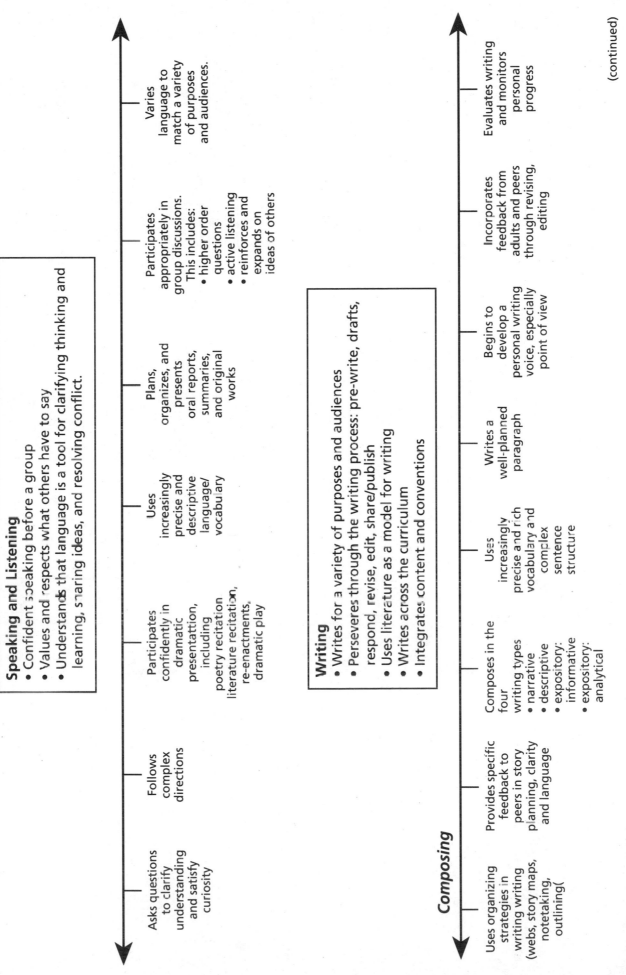

Speaking and Listening
- Confident speaking before a group
- Values and respects what others have to say
- Understands that language is a tool for clarifying thinking and learning, sharing ideas, and resolving conflict.

Varies language to match a variety of purposes and audiences.

Participates appropriately in group discussions. This includes:
- higher order questions
- active listening
- reinforces and expands on ideas of others

Plans, organizes, and presents oral reports, summaries, and original works

Uses increasingly precise and descriptive language/vocabulary

Participates confidently in dramatic presentattion, including poetry recitation literature recitation, re-enactments, dramatic play

Follows complex directions

Asks questions to clarify understanding and satisfy curiosity

Writing
- Writes for a variety of purposes and audiences
- Perseveres through the writing process: pre-write, drafts, respond, revise, edit, share/publish
- Uses literature as a model for writing
- Writes across the curriculum
- Integrates content and conventions

Evaluates writing and monitors personal progress

Incorporates feedback from adults and peers through revising, editing

Begins to develop a personal writing voice, especially point of view

Writes a well-planned paragraph

Uses increasingly precise and rich vocabulary and complex sentence structure

Composes in the four writing types
- narrative
- descriptive
- expository: informative
- expository: analytical

Provides specific feedback to peers in story planning, clarity and language

Uses organizing strategies in writing writing (webs, story maps, notetaking, outlining(

Composing

(continued)

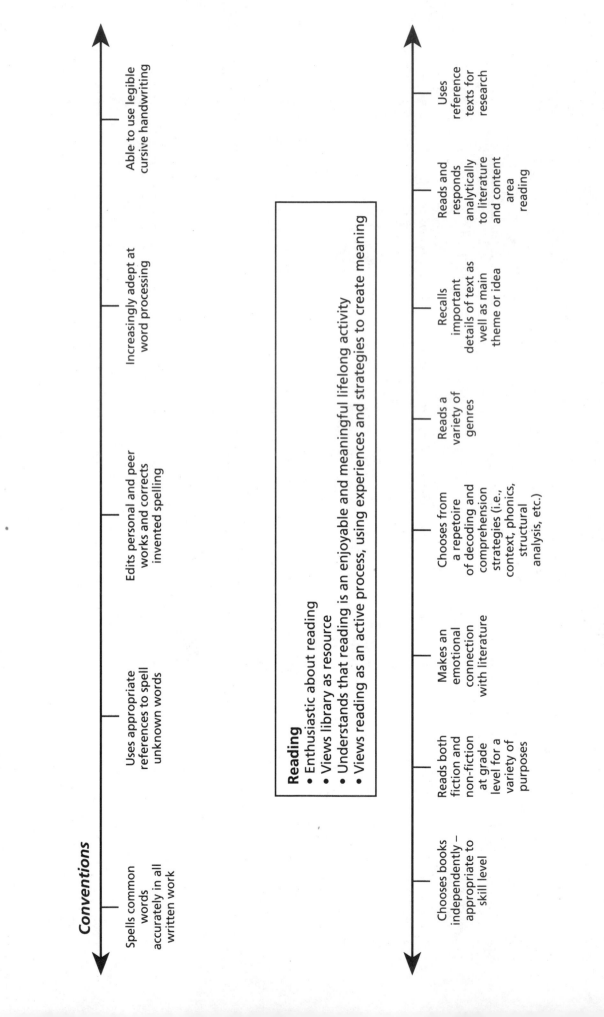

Conventions

- Spells common words accurately in all written work
- Uses appropriate references to spell unknown words
- Edits personal and peer works and corrects invented spelling
- Increasingly adept at word processing
- Able to use legible cursive handwriting

Reading
- Enthusiastic about reading
- Views library as resource
- Understands that reading is an enjoyable and meaningful lifelong activity
- Views reading as an active process, using experiences and strategies to create meaning

- Chooses books independently – appropriate to skill level
- Reads both fiction and non-fiction at grade level for a variety of purposes
- Makes an emotional connection with literature
- Chooses from a repertoire of decoding and comprehension strategies (i.e., context, phonics, structural analysis, etc.)
- Reads a variety of genres
- Recalls important details of text as well as main theme or idea
- Reads and responds analytically to literature and content area reading
- Uses reference texts for research

Reading: A Guide for Observation

WHO?

All students.

WHY?

One way to assess a child's reading ability is through careful observation of the child. By combining observational data with miscue data and the student's own self-evaluation (lists of books read, written responses to reading, self-reflection on reading strategies), teachers can create a fairly complete profile of each student as a reader.

HOW?

Reading: A Guide for Observation can be used as a checksheet, to keep brief anecdotal records, or as a combination of the two. Entries should be made for each child once per quarter to show progress throughout the year and to help provide direction for reading instruction and mediation.

WHAT ELSE?

Teachers should schedule an individual reading conference with each student at least once a quarter; more frequently for students who are not making satisfactory progress. By asking the child to choose a book to read aloud, the teacher can quickly complete this form and ascertain if the child is developing proficient reading strategies as well as an understanding of what reading is all about.

See: ANALYZING pp. 149, 151, 160, 163

Reading: A Guide for Observation was developed by Sharon Zinke, language arts specialist at Fairview School in Hayward, CA.

Reading: A Guide for Observation

Name _____ Date _____ Grade _____

1st quarter	2nd quarter	3rd quarter	4th quarter

Reads for Enjoyment: Chooses to read, has favorite books, is aware of and seeks out authors/illustrators

Reads for Meaning: Makes predictions based on cueing systems (semantic, syntactic, graphophonic), self-monitors, and corrects miscues

Projects Meaning Through Oral Expression: Reads fluently (punctuation, inflection, phrasing)

Retells Story: Makes inferences, responds to story, relates to own life (orally, in writing)

Survey in the Language Arts: Reading/Writing

WHO?

Upper-elementary and middle school students.

WHY?

Mary Kitagawa explains: "The **Survey in the Language Arts** forms support student self-evaluation and teacher assessment and invite comparison between the two. Furthermore, students accustomed to graded worksheets and various sorts of tests seem to be reassured that there are standards that hold for reading and writing workshop classrooms as well.

HOW?

"Each form takes only about fifteen minutes to complete. I make a graphic to use with an overhead projector and invite students to either mark their choice as I read aloud the descriptors in each section or to work on their own to fill out the forms.

"The first descriptors indicate great confidence and the last ones indicate a strong sense of inadequacy or lack of cooperation. Most students select descriptors from the middle of these two extremes, which differ primarily in degree of success and diligence, although both reflect functional involvement with reading and writing and reasonable participation in reading and writing workshops. If a student marks many of the last choices, I would earmark that student for some confidence building. I have not been surprised when fluent and competent students mark themselves less so, especially in writing. Experienced writers know how complex a task it is; a large measure of their motivation comes from untangling and reweaving those wonderful, terrible complexities. The more writers know about writing, the less likely they are to glibly consider themselves masters of it.

"I fill out identical forms for each student before I look at their surveys. When I compare my ratings to the students, I am amazed at the similarities of our assessments. Generally, I choose more positive descriptors than the students do. Students are very interested when I return their surveys with my version attached. They comment on the number of items we agree about and also on the times I rate them higher.

WHAT ELSE?

"It will be interesting to use the survey twice, as I intend to do this year, but even using it a single time seems to reinforce criteria both for reading and writing and for participation in reading and writing workshop."

See: REPORTING pp. 193, 198, 200

Survey in the Language Arts: Reading/Writing was developed by Mary M. Kitagawa, fifth- and sixth-grade teacher at Mark's Meadow School in Amherst, MA.

Survey in the Language Arts: Reading

Observational Rating

In each set, mark the sentence that best describes you as a reader.

Self / Teacher
(circle one)

ENJOYMENT

_____ Reading is one of my very favorite activities.
_____ I frequently choose to read for pleasure or information.
_____ Usually I read only what is assigned, but I sometimes enjoy it.
_____ I read only if I am forced to do so—never by choice.

READING NON-FICTION TEXTS

_____ I can comfortably read almost any text on any topic.
_____ I can comfortably read almost any text on a familiar topic, and I can work through many texts on unfamiliar topics.
_____ I have trouble with texts on most topics unless I read a simpler text on that topic first.
_____ I can understand only simple texts on familiar topics.

READING FICTION

_____ I read "between the lines" to get full understanding.
_____ I can usually follow the plot and many of the underlying ideas.
_____ I understand the basic plot, but I often get lost if the story takes an unexpected twist or jumps around in time, etc.
_____ I am often confused about what is happening in a story.

VOCABULARY

_____ I use context to understand unfamiliar words.
_____ Sometimes context helps me get past unfamiliar words.
_____ Unfamiliar words often slow down my reading and confuse or discourage me.
_____ I skip unfamiliar words.

USE OF RESEARCH SOURCES

_____ I use most library and reference sources independently.
_____ I use many library and reference sources with just a little guidance.
_____ I use a few library and reference sources on my own, but usually I need adult help to make the best use of them.
_____ I cannot use library or reference sources without adult help.

LITERATURE STUDY DISCUSSIONS

_____ I always come prepared and participate actively.
_____ I generally come prepared and participate.
_____ I try to come prepared and participate, but occasionally I have not done the reading on time.
_____ I almost never come prepared to participate, and often I have not done the reading on time.

READING LOGS

_____ I write personally significant and expressive reading logs.
_____ I often write reading logs that reflect my personal response.
_____ I write the required number of reading logs, but often they do not reflect a personal response.
_____ I write reading logs only when they are required and without any effort to make a personal response.

OTHER INFORMATION ABOUT YOURSELF AS A READER:

Survey in the Language Arts: Writing

Observational Rating
In each set, mark the sentence that best describes you as a reader.

Self / Teacher
(circle one)

FLUENCY

_____ I usually find it easy to express my ideas in writing.

_____ I sometimes find it easy to express my ideas in writing.

_____ I often find it hard to write, but I keep at it anyway.

_____ I have to struggle to write anything, so I never enjoy it.

TOPIC CHOICE

_____ I easily come up with a wide variety of possible topics.

_____ I frequently find topics without much difficulty.

_____ I am usually surprised and relieved when I find a good topic.

_____ I can never come up with good topics, so I just write on any old topic.

VOICE

_____ I deliberately let my own "voice" come through, if appropriate.

_____ I often find my own "voice" coming through in many of my texts.

_____ I am becoming aware of my own "voice," especially in journals.

_____ I do not know what my own "voice" is.

GENRE

_____ I write poetry, fiction, personal narratives, essays, reports, letters, reading logs, etc.

_____ I am learning to write in most of the above genre.

_____ I write in several of the above genre; I am willing to try any of them.

_____ I don't feel I can write in most of the above ways.

DEADLINES, PORTFOLIO AND JOURNAL/NOTEBOOK REQUIREMENTS

_____ I easily surpass all requirements on time or even early.

_____ I meet all requirements without reminders.

_____ I meet the minimal requirements when I am given reminders or a specially set-aside time to accomplish them.

_____ I do not fulfill requirements or follow organizational procedures.

WRITING PROCESS

_____ I decide for myself when and how to draft, revise, edit, or use strategies such as free-writing, brainstorming, etc.

_____ I am usually able to make use of the processes listed above. I use the processes above with help and guidance.

_____ I expect an adult to tell me what to do next in writing.

PROOFREADING AND EDITING

_____ I am successful and reliable in proofreading and editing.

_____ I am working on proofreading and editing skills.

_____ I can proofread and edit, but I often forget or fail to do so.

_____ I don't proofread or edit unless someone makes me do it.

OTHER INFORMATION ABOUT YOURSELF AS A WRITER:

Cumulative Writing Folders, K–5

WHO?

Kindergarten through fifth-grade students.

WHY?

Cumulative Writing Folders maintain representative samples of each student's writing for grades K–5, and provide a systematic means of documenting student development in writing. These folders will provide teachers with useful and meaningful information about students' strengths and needs. The folders also provide teachers with a broad outline of the writing program emphasized at each grade level. This will help to develop more coordination within and between grade levels.

HOW?

The folders are intended primarily as observation checklists for teachers to use as students engage in the writing process. Since writing is a developmental process, there is much overlap between the grade levels. Most items are not mastered once and for all, but become more complex each year.

There will also be great variation between different pieces of writing by the same child. The letters S (definite strength), M (moderate ability), and N (definite need) indicate whether the child has a consistent strength in an area, or only displayed that ability once. A child who consistently demonstrates an item on the checksheet in most or all writing is given an S; a student who shows the capability in some but not most writing receives M; and a student rarely showing the capability is given an N. If an item in the list is never demonstrated by the student, the space is left blank.

WHAT ELSE?

An assessment checklist can be especially helpful for new teachers who may be uncertain about the developmental range they might expect among their own students. As Ken Goodman reminds us, however, the process of constructing the checklist may be more important than its later use. Much like a shopping list we carefully construct and then leave at home, a checklist helps us think through what our goals and priorities are and enables us to be effective kidwatchers.

See: OBSERVING p. 57; ANALYZING pp. 169, 173

Cumulative Writing Folders, K–5, were developed by David Hartle-Schutte, professor of education at the University of Hawaii, Hilo.

Cumulative Writing Folder/Kindergarten

Student _____   Year _____

S = definite strength M = moderate ability N = definite need (leave blank if never accomplished)	Date 1st qtr	Date 2nd qtr	Date 3rd qtr	Date 4th qtr
Recognizes name in limited contexts (name tags, personal items)				
Writes first/last name (indicate F/L)				
Participates in prewriting activities (brainstorming, sharing, drawing, etc.)				
Uses letters to represent meaning (may be random use of letters)				
Systematic use of letters/words to represent meaning (beg. & end letters)				
Labels pictures with words/sentences (own writing/dictation to teacher)				
Uses approximate & standard spelling				
Selects writing as a choice				
Uses writing spontaneously				
Reads some environmental print				
Reads pattern/predictable books				
Chooses own writing topics				
Reads back own writing				
Shares own writing				
Revises own writing				
Writing expresses complete ideas				
Writing has logical sequence (time, cause & effect, etc.)				
Handwriting legible				
Published final draft				

Comments, strengths, needs (include references to writing samples in folder):

_____

_____

_____

Cumulative Writing Folder/Grade 1

Student _____   Year _____

S = definite strength M = moderate ability N = definite need (leave blank if never accomplished)	Date 1st qtr	Date 2nd qtr	Date 3rd qtr	Date 4th qtr
Writes first/last name (indicate F/L)				
Uses letters to represent meaning (may be very non-standard)				
Systematic use of letters/words to represent meaning				
Labels pictures with words/sentences (indicates own writing or dictation)				
Uses approximate & standard spelling				
Selects writing as a choice				
Uses writing spontaneously (during play/informal situations)				
Reads environmental print (product packages, signs. etc.)				
Reads pattern/predictable books				
Participates in prewriting activities (brainstorming, drawing, sharing, etc.)				
Chooses own writing topics				
Reads back own writing				
Shares own writing (1st/final drafts, individual/group)				
Revises own writing for sentence structure (w/help or independently)				
Writing expresses complete ideas (sentence/story level, 1st/final draft)				
Writing has logical sequence (time, cause/effect, etc.)				
Handwriting legible				
Published final draft (personal experience, imaginative, poem, communication)				
Edits for spelling, capitalization, punctuation				

Comments, strengths, needs (include references to writing samples in folder):

_____

_____

_____

Cumulative Writing Folder/Grade 2

Student _____   Year _____

S = definite strength M = moderate ability N = definite need (leave blank if never accomplished)	Date 1st qtr	Date 2nd qtr	Date 3rd qtr	Date 4th qtr
Systematic use of letters or words to represent meaning				
Labels pictures with words/sentences				
Uses approximate & standard spelling				
Selects writing as a choice (during free choice)				
Uses writing spontaneously (notes to teacher, friends, in play)				
Participates in prewriting activities (brainstorming, discussing, drawing)				
Chooses own writing topics/selects approp. titles (individual & group)				
Reads back own writing				
Shares own writing (1st/final drafts, individual/group)				
Revises own writing for sentence structure (w/others or independently)				
Writing expresses complete ideas (sentence & story level)				
Writing of sufficient, appropriate length				
Writing has logical sequence (time, cause/effect, etc.)				
Edits for mechanics (spelling, indentation, punctuation, grammar, capitals)				
Handwriting legible				
Published final draft:				
personal experience narrative _____				
imaginative story _____				
report _____				
communication (letter, note, etc.) _____				

Comments, strengths, needs (include references to writing samples in folder):

_____

_____

_____

_____

Cumulative Writing Folder/Grade 3

Student _____   Year _____

S = definite strength M = moderate ability N = definite need (leave blank if never accomplished)	Date 1st qtr	Date 2nd qtr	Date 3rd qtr	Date 4th qtr
Selects writing as a choice (during free choice)				
Participates in prewriting activities (brainstorming, webbing, drawing, etc.)				
Chooses own writing topics				
Uses approximate & standard spelling in first drafts				
Shares own writing (in small or large groups)				
Revises own writing for meaning (w/others or independently)				
Revises own writing for sentence structure (w/others or independently)				
Writing expresses complete ideas (writing sentences & story as whole)				
Writing has logical sequence (time, cause/effect, etc. in final draft)				
Uses descriptive language				
Edits for mechanics (spelling, indentation, punctuation, grammar, capitals)				
Handwriting legible (in final draft, manuscript or cursive)				
Published final draft:				
personal experience narrative _____				
imaginative story _____				
report _____				
communication (letter, note, etc.) _____				
poem _____				

Comments, strengths, needs (include references to writing samples in folder):

_____

_____

_____

_____

_____

_____

Cumulative Writing Folder/Grade 4

Student _____   Year _____

S = definite strength M = moderate ability N = definite need (leave blank if never accomplished)	Date 1st qtr	Date 2nd qtr	Date 3rd qtr	Date 4th qtr
Participates in prewriting activities (brainstorm, web, discuss, draw)				
Chooses writing topics, narrows topic appropriately (independently, w/help)				
Uses approximate & standard spelling in first drafts				
Shares own writing (in small/large groups)				
Revises own writing for meaning (independently, w/others)				
Revises own writing for sentence structure (independently, w/help)				
Expresses complete ideas within sentence and story as whole (in final draft)				
Writing has logical sequence				
Uses descriptive language				
Writes effective beginnings				
Writes effective endings				
Edits for mechanics (spelling, caps., punctuation, grammar, handwriting)				
Published final draft:				
personal experience narrative _____				
imaginative story _____				
report _____				
communication (letter, note, etc.) _____				
poem _____				

Comments, strengths, needs (include references to writing samples in folder):

_____

_____

_____

_____

_____

Cumulative Writing Folder/Grade 5

Student_____   Year _____

S = definite strength M = moderate ability N = definite need (leave blank if never accomplished)	Date 1st qtr	Date 2nd qtr	Date 3rd qtr	Date 4th qtr
Participates in prewriting activities (brainstorm, discuss, draw, list . . .)				
Chooses own writing topics (narrows topic appropriately)				
Shares own writing (first and later drafts) (in small/large groups)				
Revises own writing for meaning				
Revises own writing for sentence structure (independently, w/others)				
Expresses complete ideas within sentence & story as whole (in final draft)				
Writing has logical sequence				
Uses descriptive language				
Writes effective beginnings				
Middle of text well integrated with beginning and end				
Writes effective endings				
Develops characters well				
Uses dialogue effectively				
Uses other literary techniques (metaphor, flashback, foreshadowing)				
Edits for mechanics (spelling, caps., punctuation, grammar, handwriting)				
Published final draft:				
personal experience narrative _____				
imaginative story _____				
report _____				
communication (letter, note, etc.) _____				
poem _____				
summary _____				

Comments, strengths, needs (include references to writing samples in folder):

_____

_____

_____

A Process Checklist for Writing · Primary Writing Goals

WHO?

A Process Checklist for Writing was developed for all students, K–8. The **Primary Writing Goals** serve primary students.

WHY?

In writing-process classrooms, teachers are equally interested in the process and the product of their students' writing. These two forms assess the process in which students participate as they write, although the forms also touch upon writing aspects reflected in the students' writing.

HOW?

These are forms that teachers complete over a period of weeks as they observe their students at work during writer's workshop.

WHAT ELSE?

Teachers may want to share the completed checklists with their students, sharing their observations and soliciting students' opinions about their own writing process. It may be helpful to compare the two; do teachers' and students' assessment match up? If not, how do they differ and what is the significance of the difference?

See: ANALYZING pp. 169, 173

A Process Checklist for Writing was developed by Maureen White, K–8 writing coordinator for Haverhill Public Schools in Haverhill, MA.

Primary Writing Goals was developed by Kathleen Cain, Cathy Carter, Nycki Guest, Jan Haddick, Rose Hammond, Kay Keeley, and Carol Munier, teachers of primary grades at Lowell Elementary School in Missoula, MT.

A Process Checklist for Writing

Child's Name _____ Date _____ Grade _____

Does this student...

1. Write during designated time?
   ☐ Always   ☐ Sometimes   ☐ Rarely

2. Use constructive strategies for getting drafts started?
   ☐ Always   ☐ Sometimes   ☐ Rarely

3. Take the conference period seriously?
   a. Is willing to help classmates by listening to their drafts?
   b. Realizes other children may have meaningful suggestions?
   ☐ Always   ☐ Sometimes   ☐ Rarely

4. Show growth in his/her understanding of the difference between revising (i.e. adding on) and editing?
   ☐ Quite a bit   ☐ Some   ☐ Very Little

5. Use the support systems in the classroom (manual guidelines, spelling aids, dictionaries)?
   ☐ Frequently   ☐ Occasionally   ☐ Infrequently

6. View revision as part of a healthy writing process?
   ☐ Yes   ☐ At times   ☐ No

7. Actively participate during sharing?
   ☐ Almost always   ☐ On occasion   ☐ Always

Primary Writing Goals

Student Name _____ Teacher _____ Date _____

Year _____	1st qtr	2nd qtr	3rd qtr	4th qtr
Writing Approaches				
• uses pictures to tell story				
• uses scribbles to signify meaning				
• copies environmental print				
• uses random letters to signify meaning				
• uses inventive spelling				
• uses conventional spelling				
• attempts unknown words by using language patterns				
• uses left-to-right movement				
Comprehension Approaches				
• formulates ideas for personal writing				
• builds a story line (beginning, middle, end)				
• stays on topic				
• uses new vocabulary terms in writing				
• expands descriptive language in writing				
• revises for clarification of meaning				
Behavioral Approaches				
• takes risks				
• enjoys writing				
• writes independently				
• sees self as a writer				
• sits for a time and writes				
• writes for different purposes				
• writes for different audiences				
• is developing correct use of capitalization, punctuation, and sentence structure				
• is beginning to edit for mechanics				
• shares writing—published and unpublished				
• likes to have others edit writing				
• likes to edit work of others				

Observed Reading Behavior · Fall/Winter Reading and Writing Assessment · Fall/Winter Math Assessment

WHO? _____

Kindergarten students.

WHY? _____

Joan Foley explains: "I use the **Observed Reading Behavior**, the **Fall Reading and Writing Assessment**, and the **Fall Math Assessment** sheets for the fall conference. It allows the parents to see what I look for and how I evaluate. I use the **Winter Reading and Writing Assessment** and the **Winter Math Assessment**, which are slightly different than the fall assessments, for the winter conference. The children progress so much at this time of the year, and the parents love seeing their child's development!

HOW? _____

"At the end of the school year I conference one more time with parents. It gives a nice closure to the year. At this time I give the parents their child's portfolio that the child has edited. The child decides what goes into his or her portfolio: the child's published books, journals, art projects, math stories, etc.

"At the end of each season the children look through their portfolios and have a delightful time seeing their special accomplishments. This is when they decide what they want to keep in their portfolios and what they will take home; however, I insist that certain items be kept in the portfolio. At the end of the school year a final math and reading composite and a sample of the child's writing are given to the first-grade teachers. The rest is put into their 'Kindergarten Portfolio' to be taken home at conference time.

WHAT ELSE? _____

"Because the children want to show their work to their families as soon as they complete it, I attach the following note to their work explaining that the project has to be returned to school so that it can be placed in their portfolio":

> Note to parents:
> Look what I made today! This will be kept in my portfolio, which is where I will put the work I want to keep forever. I wanted to show this to you, but Mrs. Foley wants me to please return it to school tomorrow. Thanks!

See: MONITORING p. 9; OBSERVING pp. 62, 93; ANALYZING p. 145; INTERACTING p. 116

Observed Reading Behavior, Fall/Winter Reading and Writing Assessment, and Fall/Winter Math Assessment were developed by Joan Foley, who taught kindergarten and currently teaches third grade at Rockland School in Libertyville, IL.

Observed Reading Behavior

Name _____ Date _____ Grade _____

_____ 1. Locates the front cover of a book

_____ 2. Locates the back cover of a book

_____ 3. Locates the title of a book

_____ 4. Knows what an author does

_____ 5. Knows what an illustrator does

_____ 6. Can point to a word

_____ 7. Can point to the illustrations

_____ 8. Can point to the space between words

_____ 9. Can find the page number

_____ 10. Points to the top line

_____ 11. Points to the beginning word on a page

_____ 12. Points to bottom line

_____ 13. "Reads" book in proper sequence (left to right)

_____ 14. Mock reads

_____ 15. Enjoys reading and looking at books

_____ 16. Enjoys checking out books

_____ 17. Listens during story time

_____ 18. Wants to write words with pictures

_____ 19. Is comfortable with invented spelling

Fall Reading and Writing Assessment

Name _____ Date _____ Grade _____

- Draws pictures only

  ☐ NEVER ☐ SELDOM ☐ FREQUENTLY

- Scribbles and prints mock letters

  ☐ NEVER ☐ SELDOM ☐ FREQUENTLY

- Writes conventional words

  ☐ NEVER ☐ SELDOM ☐ FREQUENTLY

- Copies words from classroom

  ☐ NEVER ☐ SELDOM ☐ FREQUENTLY

- Will ask how to spell a word

  ☐ NEVER ☐ SELDOM ☐ FREQUENTLY

- Is comfortable writing from teacher spelling

  ☐ NEVER ☐ SELDOM ☐ FREQUENTLY

LETTER AND SOUND INVENTORY

Letter	Sound	Can find in text
M	_____	_____
T	_____	_____
F	_____	_____
H	_____	_____
N	_____	_____
B	_____	_____
P	_____	_____

INVENTED SPELLING

Yes	No	
_____	_____	will write letter(s) for beginning sounds
_____	_____	will write letters for middle sounds
_____	_____	will write letters for ending sounds

Winter Reading and Writing Assessment

Name _____ Date _____ Grade _____

1. Enjoys working at the writing table

        ☐ Seldom   ☐ Frequently   ☐ Always

2. Enjoys drawing and writing in journal

        ☐ Seldom   ☐ Frequently   ☐ Always

3. Copies from classroom model on own paper

        ☐ Seldom   ☐ Frequently   ☐ Always

4. Copies dictated words (will ask how to spell a word)

        ☐ Seldom   ☐ Frequently   ☐ Always

5. Letter and sound inventory

Recognizes letter	Recognizes sound	Can find in text
L A C G I J S W	L A C G I J S W	L A C G I J S W

6. Developmental spelling and writing

_____ will write beginning sounds

_____ will write letters for middle sounds

_____ will write letters for ending sounds

_____ will write a complete thought

_____ puts space between words

_____ uses capital letters

_____ uses ending marks

7. Observed reading behavior

_____ makes up books in the classroom

_____ makes up a front and back cover to book

_____ includes title in book

_____ provides space between written words

_____ uses developmental spelling

_____ uses beginning punctuation

Fall Math Assessment

Name _____ Date _____ Grade _____

1. Rote counting to:

2. Count after me: 3, 4
   11, 12
   21, 22

3. Count backwards from:

4. Count 5 only:

5. Which has 5:

6. Conservation of number task:

_____ understands 1:1 correspondence

(spread second row out)

_____ uses spatial perception

_____ conserves number by trial and error

_____ conserves number using logic

7. Instant recognition: 3   4   5   6

8. Which is closer to: **6**   **8**   **4**
   5   9   2   10   10   6

9. Produce objects: 5
   8
   10
   12

10. Print numbers 1-10:

Winter Math Assessment

Name _____ Date _____ Grade _____

1. Enjoys playing with manipulatives

  ☐ Seldom ☐ Frequently ☐ Often

2. Likes to build and design with manipulatives

  ☐ Seldom ☐ Frequently ☐ Often

3. Participates during calendar activities

  ☐ Seldom ☐ Frequently ☐ Often

4. Observes patterns in classroom

  ☐ Seldom ☐ Frequently ☐ Often

5. Sees relationships and shares ideas

  ☐ Seldom ☐ Frequently ☐ Often

6. Shares ideas with numbers

  ☐ Seldom ☐ Frequently ☐ Often

7. Uses numbers to investigate

  ☐ Seldom ☐ Frequently ☐ Often

Literacy Environment Evaluation

WHO?

All teachers and administrators.

WHY?

Teachers may choose to use the **Literacy Environment Evaluation** sheet for self-evaluation at various times during the school year. It will serve as a reminder of the functions of a literate environment. Administrators may choose to use it during observations in conjunction with more detailed observational notes and discussions with teachers.

HOW?

The Literacy Environment Evaluation form is not all-inclusive. This observation sheet shows a variety of options that can be useful in promoting the development of literacy. The presence of all or most of these items in the classroom does not guarantee a literate environment. Nor does the absence of any single item or group of items indicate a poor literate environment. More important is the quality of interactions among students and between teachers and students.

WHAT ELSE?

This form has been used successfully in teacher education classes, providing student teachers with guidelines for creating their own literate classroom environments. Unfortunately, not all are able to do their student teaching in richly literate, student-centered classrooms; this checklist highlights the features of such an environment, which they can work to create once they have their own classrooms.

See: INTERACTING pp. 131, 134; REPORTING pp. 214

Literacy Environment Evaluation was developed by David Hartle-Schutte, professor of education at the University of Hawaii, Hilo.

Literacy Environment Evaluation

Name _____   Date _____

Is the functional use of print for the entire classroom observed in:

Daily messages, schedules, assignments, notices
(chalkboard, bulletin board, or charts)   _____

Labels (on cabinets, containers, equipment)
(to identify needed materials and storage areas)   _____

Current child-written messages, labels, etc.   _____

Bulletin boards, etc., related to class activities   _____

Sign-up, sign-in, sign-out sheets   _____

Different charts, including:
    classroom rules   _____
    songs   _____
    nursery rhymes   _____
    class or group original stories   _____
    calendar   _____
    class log or diary   _____
    recipes   _____
    project directions   _____
    instructions for pet care, etc.   _____

Physical arrangement of classroom and materials
conducive to literacy development   _____

Is the functional use of print on an individual basis observable in:

Student labeling of own work (including but not limited to name)   _____

Individual journals or log books   _____

Student-published materials   _____

Physical and temporal access to a variety of writing materials and
equipment (markers, pencils, pens, chalk, paper, chalkboard, etc.)   _____

Letter writing or pen pals   _____

Individual messages to parents   _____

Teacher notes to students   _____

Student opportunity and encouragement to write   _____

(continued)

Is a variety of printed material available/accessible?
   children's literature _____

   references (dictionaries, encyclopedias, lists, charts, pictures, etc.) _____

   Non-fiction information books _____

   Miscellaneous print (comics, newspapers, maps, globes, student authored books, magazines) _____

   Frequent opportunities to read self-selected material _____

Is the modeling of literacy behaviors by the teacher observable?

   Writing: notes to parents _____
         notes to students _____
         notes to other adults _____
         notes to self _____
         lists, signs, etc. for classroom revisions and edits _____

   Reading: communication from others _____
         books to children _____
         notices, announcements, etc. to kids _____
         other materials to self _____

   Attitudes: tries new things _____
         makes and points out own errors _____
         refers to books or other references _____
         models enjoyment of reading and writing _____
         responds to message over form _____
         encourages child to attempt reading and writing _____

Other areas
   Is there a reliance on basals and other textbooks? _____
   Is there heavy use of ditto masters and workbooks? _____
   Is there emphasis on sequential skills and "mastery"? _____
   Is there emphasis on immediate error correction? _____
   Are all students engaged in identical activities? _____

Comments:

Scale of Writing Development · Scale of Emergent Reading · Response to Literature Scale · Reading Record for Conferences

WHO?

Primary and elementary students.

WHY?

Portfolio assessment is part of the movement toward authentic instruction and assessment. As teachers are exposed to holistic philosophies and use more authentic materials such as children's literature for instruction, their goals and methods change. These changes in curricular orientation bring with them changes in assessment of student progress.

HOW?

Blackburn Elementary School teachers created the **Scale of Writing Development** from children's writing samples. From Sulzby's emergent reading scale (1985) and samples of reading behaviors, they developed the **Scale of Emergent Reading**. Each grade level also had checklists on which to record children's progress, but gone were the traditional ratings of children as outstanding, average, or below average students.

The **Response to Literature Scale** emerged from the school's move toward a literature-based reading curriculum. Teachers moved into portfolio assessment as a way of documenting children's progress on these schoolwide scales. Three different types of information were gathered:

COLLECTION AND ANALYSIS OF STUDENT WORK (ARTIFACTS)

Included in the working portfolio artifacts were writing folders, reading response journals, dialogue journals, day books, projects, and writing notebooks. The purpose of working portfolios was to provide a place for students to collect and store their ongoing work for easy retrieval. Analysis of these collected artifacts became critical as teachers tried to determine children's levels of performance for the portfolio scales and as they communicated to parents about children's progress. Parents needed to have their children's work interpreted for them. At least once a marking period it helped to sit down and systematically analyze children's growth.

Collecting children's work demonstrates that the children are progressing. Especially if teachers analyze what is in the student portfolios, parents can see that their children's writings, for example, are getting longer, more thoughtful, more detailed, more interesting, and easier to read throughout the year. Similarly, in reading, it can be pointed out that children are reading more, reading longer and more challenging books, and responding more thoughtfully to what they read over time.

STUDENT REFLECTION AND SELF-EVALUATION

The most vital aspect of assessment in a classroom where children bear much of the responsibility for the curriculum is student reflection and self-evaluation. The concept of ownership of the curriculum includes assessment as well. If children are to become autonomous learners, they must learn to assess what they have learned and how they learn best. Teachers should routinely ask children why the work they selected as their best work was in fact their best work. One way a number of teachers chose to help children reflect upon their work was to have them select their best work for a "showcase portfolio." Showcase portfolios are typically folders or expandable file folders decorated by the children. They provided a vehicle for the children to reflect upon their own work and to hear others reflect upon their work as a strategy for learning what constitutes exemplary work for them.

OBSERVATIONS, CHECKLISTS, AND SCALES

Three kinds of data were gathered by teachers: observational data, checklist data, and interview or conference data. Teachers had concerns about what and how much to record for each child. Two guidelines emerged. First, it is important to record information on process that is not readily available elsewhere, such as in artifacts or checklists. Second, while it is important to note observations on each child, it is also important to be selective so that the notes that are taken are actually useful to inform instruction and assess progress.

Checklists help expedite data collection if there is information that is important to gather on every child in the classroom. Fisher (1989) lists several kinds of information that is important to observe while children are reading: *General observations*—interest, enjoyment, concentration, sense of story, telling a story from pictures, retelling a story; *Conventions of print*—book handling, awareness of and attention to print, reading level (from scale of emergent reading). Blackburn teacher, Shirley Cochrane, adopted the **Reading Record for Conferences** to help monitor her students' developing reading abilities.

WHAT ELSE?

Parents need to be an integral part of the assessment process. At Blackburn, parents are invited to send notes about what children do at home as well as artifacts for the teacher portfolio. At the end of a marking period, the school uses a questionnaire to systematically solicit parental input about what they are noticing at home regarding their children's progress. The questionnaires can either be returned to school with the children or brought with them to their conference with the teacher. In this way, parents become an integral part of the portfolio system.

— Adapted from "One School's Adventure into Portfolio Assessment" (*Language Arts*, 68, December 1991).

References
Fisher. B. 1989. Assessing emergent and initial readers. *Teaching K–8*. Nov./Dec., 56–58.
Sulzby, E. 1985. Children's emergent reading of favorite storybooks: A developmental study. *Reading Research Quarterly*, 20, 458–481.

See: OBSERVING p. 84; REPORTING pp. 219, 222, 224, 226, 228

Scale of Writing Development, Scale of Emergent Reading, Response to Literature Scale, and Reading Record for Conferences were developed by Linda Leonard Lamme, professor at the University of Florida, Gainesville, and Cecilia Hysmith, principal of Blackburn Elementary School in Manatee County, FL.

Scale of Writing Development

Level 11: The child—
_____ uses a variety of strategies for revision and editing.
_____ uses writing techniques to build suspense, create humor, etc.

Level 10: The child—
_____ willingly revises and edits.
_____ writes creatively and imaginatively.
_____ writes original poetry.
_____ writes clearly; the message makes sense.
_____ uses commas, quotation marks, and apostrophes.

Level 9: The child—
_____ includes details or dialogue, a sense of humor, or other emotions.
_____ retells a familiar story or follows the pattern of a known story or poem.
_____ uses more conventional spelling.
_____ willingly revises.

Level 8: The child—
_____ writes a short story with a beginning, a middle, and an end.
_____ writes for several different purposes (narrative, expository, and persuasive).
_____ revises by adding to the story.
_____ begins to use punctuation.

Level 7: The child—
_____ writes the start of a story.
_____ uses both phonics and sight strategies to spell words.
_____ writes several short sentences.

Level 6: The child—
_____ invents spellings.
_____ presents a story that is a single factual statement.
_____ presents a message that is understandable.

Level 5: The child—
_____ labels drawings.
_____ uses letters that have some connection to sounds.
_____ writes lists.
_____ separates words with a space or marker.
_____ writes a message.
_____ writes familiar words.

Level 4: The child—
_____ repeats message.
_____ has a message concept and tells you what the message is.
_____ uses letters that don't match sounds.
_____ writes alphabet letter strings.

Level 3: The child—
_____ copies words he/she sees around the room.
_____ writes alphabet letters and mock letters in a line across the page.

Level 2: The child—
_____ writes alphabet and mock letters scattered around the page.
_____ writes mock letters.
_____ pretends to write.

Level 1: The child—
_____ attempts to write in scribbles or draws patterns.

Scale of Emergent Reading

Level 11: The child—
_____ reads fluently from books and other materials

Level 10: The child—
_____ seeks out new sources of information

Level 9: The child—
_____ uses context clues, sentence structure, structural analysis, and phonic analysis
to read new passages.
_____ can read easy books.

Level 8: The child—
_____ reads unfamiliar stories haltingly, with little adult assistance.

Level 7: The child—
_____ reads familiar stories fluently.

Level 6: The child—
_____ reads word for word

Level 5: The child—
_____ memorizes text and can pretend to "read" story.

Level 4: The child—
_____ participates in reading by supplying rhyming words and some predictable text.

Level 3: The child—
_____ talks about each picture (not story, really).

Level 2: The child—
_____ watches pictures as adult reads.

Level 1: The child—
_____ listens to stories but is not looking at pages.

Response to Literature Scale

Level 7: The child—
_____ develops criteria to evaluate the book: "This is a great mystery because I couldn't figure out the answer till the last page and because you really feel like you are there."

Level 6: The child—
_____ generalizes about the book with comments about the theme, type of book, or author's purpose for writing it: "I guess being a friend means doing something you don't want to do just to be helpful to someone."

Level 5: The child—
_____ analyzes something about the book (plot, setting, characters, illustration): "Ahmed is young to have a responsible job and old to just be learning how to write his name."

Level 4: The child—
_____ relates the book to his or her experiences or to other books: "I went on a train ride once" or "Katie Morag reminds me of Sal in _One Morning in Maine._"

Level 3: The child—
_____ explains why he or she likes or does not like a book. "I like it because it is funny."

Level 2: The child—
_____ tells how he or she likes the book.
_____ asks you to "read it again."
_____ comments "It was good, " or "It was okay."

Level 1: The child—
_____ offers no response to literature voluntarily.

Note:
Responses are higher when they are child-generated than when they are teacher-assigned.
Responses are higher when they involve emotions.
Responses are higher when they involve taking action as well as discussion.
Responses are higher when they are multidimensional (dramatic, artistic, and action-oriented).
Responses are higher when they lead to further reading.

Reading Record for Conferences

Name _____ Date _____

Title of Book _____

Familiar text?	Y	N
Chose appropriate reading level?	Y	N
Student influenced selection?	Y	N
Teacher influenced selection?	Y	N
Read fluently?	Y	N
Read for meaning?	Y	N
Noticed miscues that interfered with meaning?	Y	N
Read word for word?	Y	N

Observation of Miscue Strategies

Used context clues?	Y	N
Used picture clues?	Y	N
Used beginning/ending sounds?	Y	N
Used other phonetic clues?	Y	N
Self-corrected?	Y	N

Observation of Self-Correction Attitudes

Reads eagerly?	Y	N
Comfortable with reading?	Y	N
Guessed at meaning?	Y	N
Willing to take risks?	Y	N

Observation of Comprehension

Retold story?	Y	N
easily?	Y	N
Responded to text?	Y	N
easily?	Y	N

Response to Reading

Author: _____

Illustrations: Liked?	Y	N

Why? _____

_____

Why do you think the author wrote this story? _____

_____

_____

Burke Reading Interview ·
Reading Interest Inventory

WHO? ————————————————————————————————————

Students of all ages, parents, and community members.

WHY? ————————————————————————————————————

Personal interviews with students, parents, or community members provide information that can be used to discover (1) what individuals believe reading and writing are and how it affects their lives, (2) what kinds of materials people have in their homes that provide a literate environment for members of the family, (3) what kinds of literacy experiences people engage in, (4) what attitudes parents and community members have about the role of literacy in their lives and how they believe this impacts their children, (5) how children and adults respond to reading and writing experiences, (6) ways in which people define themselves and their family as literate, and more.

HOW? ————————————————————————————————————

Interviewing individuals or family groups about literacy can be done by students, teachers, or researchers. The kinds of questions asked depend on the puposes for wanting to know the information. Interviewers need to participate in serious discussions and simulations about ways to conduct interviews that consider ethical issues as well as concerns, such as the best kinds of questions to use, how to conduct the interviews, and what problems might arise during the interview. Interviewers must respect the people they are questioning. It is important to explain to those being questioned the purposes behind such experiences.

When bilingual or multilingual people are being interviewed, it helps to have a proficient speaker of the other language(s) participate. Not all questions in one language translate easily into another. Good questioners watch carefully who they are interviewing to see whether they are being understood and adjust their questions accordingly. Also, if they begin to realize that the person they are questioning is uncomfortable, it is best to terminate the interview and plan it for another time.

WHAT ELSE? ————————————————————————————————

The questions on the **Reading Interest Inventory** could be completed at school or sent home for the parent and student to do together. For both this and the **Burke Reading Interview,** it is helpful to record the interviews and to take notes. If possible, a second person can be a quiet observer taking notes to gain a more complete picture of the interview setting. This is, of course, explained honestly to the people being interviewed. If the persons being interviewed seem the least bit uncomfortable, it is helpful to tell them how the information will be used and that the notes and audio recording will be given to them to listen to and change before the information is used.

See: INTERACTING p. 121

Burke Reading Interview was developed by Carolyn Burke, professor of reading in the College of Education, University of Indiana, Bloomington.

Reading Interest Inventory was developed by Tucson TAWL.

Burke Reading Interview

The interview should be conducted in an informal setting, relatively free of interruption. Notations of the student's responses can be made in an anecdotal record or in other suitable form.

INTERVIEW QUESTIONS

1. When you are reading and you come to something you don't know, what do you do? Do you ever do anything else?

2. Do you think that (ask teacher's name) is a good reader? Who is a good reader that you know?

3. What makes him/her a good reader?

4. Do you think that she/he ever comes to something she/he doesn't know when she/he is reading?

5. IF YES: When she/he does come to something she/he doesn't know, what do you think she/he does about it?

6. If you knew that someone was having difficulty reading, how would you help them?

7. What would your teacher do to help that person?

8. How did you learn to read? What did (they/you) do to help you learn?

9. What would you like to do better as a reader?

10. Do you think that you are a good reader?

Reading Interest Inventory

QUESTIONS RELATED TO BOOKS
1. What is the name of your favorite book that someone has read aloud to you?
2. What is the name of your favorite book or story that you have read for yourself?
3. What kind of stories and books do you like to hear read aloud to you?
4. What is the title of a book you have read recently that you like the best?
5. What is the title of the best book you have ever read?
6. What are the names of some of your favorite authors?
7. What is the worst book you remember reading? Why didn't you like it?
8. How much do you like to read?

☐ very much   ☐ quite a lot   ☐ not very much   ☐ not at all

9. Do you like to talk to others about books you read?
10. What do you do when you decide you don't like the book you're reading?
11. Which of the following kinds of books would you like to read? Have you ever read any? How often?

☐ football stories   ☐ historical novels   ☐ scientific experiments   ☐ animal stories
☐ baseball stories   ☐ mystery stories   ☐ poetry   ☐ nature stories
☐ basketball stories   ☐ career stories   ☐ teenagers' problems   ☐ biographies and autobiographies
☐ adventure stories   ☐ science fiction   ☐ do-it-yourself manuals   of famous people

12. What kind of people do you like to read about?
13. How do you like books to end?
14. Has reading a book ever helped you feel better about a problem you had?

QUESTIONS RELATED TO READING SUPPORT AT HOME AND READING MATERIALS OTHER THAN BOOKS
1. What are the names of some of the books you have at home?
2. What are the names of your two favorite television programs?
3. What is the name of your favorite comic book?
4. What part of the newspaper do you like to read the best? How do you read each?
5. What magazines do you read regularly?

QUESTIONS RELATED TO LIBRARY USE
1. Have you ever been to the library with a member of your family? Do you go by yourself? How often?
2. Do you have a library card?
3. How many books have you checked out from the library during the last month?

OBSERVING LANGUAGE USE IN PROGRESS
1. Does the student share his or her writing, or does he or she read with others?
2. What happens when the student produces, sees, or hears a miscue?
3. Does the student use outlines or other graphic representations?
4. Does the student use resources such as books, charts, signs, dictionaries, or other people to spell words or get ideas?
5. Is the student engrossed in the language event or easily distracted?

THE FOLLOWING QUESTIONS FOCUS ESPECIALLY ON YOUNGER CHILDREN
6. Does the student draw before writing?
7. Does the student have a concept of words (i.e., printed units bounded by space), sentence, story, etc.?
8. Does the student understand directionality?
9. Is the student audibly sounding out letters or words?
10. How does the student use the space on the paper?

OBSERVING SIGNS OF LANGUAGE DEVELOPMENT
1. Do miscues reveal signs of growth, i.e., movement toward convention, synonym substitutions, etc.?
2. Does the student ask about conventions, or is the student overly concerned with conventions?
3. Does the student revise or self-correct during language use?
4. What type of changes does the student make when revising or self-correcting?

Reading Environmental Print

WHO?

All developing readers.

WHY?

Reading Environmental Print reveals children's knowledge of environmentally embedded print and supporting contextual cues.

HOW?

Labels selected from an array of household, toy, food product, market, or street signs, are mounted on tag board (half of a file folder), placed in a three-ring binder, and shown one at a time to students by flipping through the binder. The collection of items could also include gas station signs, food items, TV shows, whole labels—such as the front panel of a Rice Krispies box—and partial labels—the major print from a label, with all familiar pictures, designs, and less significant print removed, thereby allowing teachers to see the degree to which other parts of the context influence children's reading. Item selection should reflect the local environment and the present time period.

Children's responses to the items can be categorized to establish their knowledge of environmental print and to show development over time. For example, the child's response can be coded as including the actual product name or only part of the name. Other common responses might include providing generic names for specific ones, such as *cereal* for Rice Krispies. Some children respond with names of parallel items; for example, saying Raisin Bran for Rice Krispies. But it is also interesting to note how seldom, if ever, any child provides an unrelated item such as Raisin Bran for McDonald's. By presenting these tasks to children at the beginning and the end of a year, teachers can evaluate the degree to which children have grown in their responses to environmental print.

WHAT ELSE?

Some teachers like to prepare for this task with the actual items from the supermarket or comparable items that are available from commercial play stores. Others like to take the children on a walk through a local supermarket or through the neighborhood or school and look at the signs embedded in the real setting. The latter, which might be called a Reading Safari, is a good experience even for older primary and middle-grade students. Some teachers have each child write in a personal "Things I Can Read" book when they return from their Reading Safari, and they add to this book throughout the school year. Bilingual students can look for signs in both of their languages. This helps to show that some communities include the print of more than one language.

Reference

Goodman, Y., Altwerger, B., and Marek, A. 1989. *Print awareness in preschool children: The development of literacy in preschool children.* Occasional Paper no. 4. Program in Language and Literacy, College of Education, University of Arizona, Tucson.

See: INTERACTING pp. 104, 111, 116

Reading Environmental Print was developed by Yetta M. Goodman, professor of Reading, Language, and Culture at the School of Education, University of Arizona, Tucson.

Reading Environmental Print

Name _____ Date _____ Grade _____

Initial questioning

1. Have you ever seen this before? (to determine if the child has had previous contact with the printed stimuli.)
2. Where?
3. What do you think that is? (to determine the child's response to the printed stimuli.)
4. What do you think that says?
5. How do you know? (to determine why the child responded the way he/she did.)
6. Why did you say that?
7. What makes you think so?
8. What tells you what it says? (to determine what stimuli the child is responding to.)
9. Show me with your finger where it says . . .

Expanding and exploratory questioning

1. What else does this say? (to determine as thoroughly as possible what stimuli the children are reacting to).
2. How do you know?
3. What can you tell me about this?
4. Show me with your finger what you are looking at.

"Show me where it says"

Techniques to employ:
1. Ask open-ended questions about printed stimuli in a situational context. Vary your language to see if different questions produce different responses.
2. Be careful to ask all questions for each item. Make sure that you point to each item and say, "Show me with your finger where it says . . ."
3. Try not to provide subject with information. For example, "Do you like to eat this?"

Some don'ts

1. Avoid asking yes/no questions such as "Can you . . . ?" or "Do you know . . . ?"
2. Don't be specific in your questioning. Ask general questions that might elicit language from the child.
3. Don't stop at "I don't know." Follow up with other questions.
4. Don't wear out the same question. Develop the art of rephrasing and paraphrasing.
5. Don't refer to the stimulus as a "picture." Words like "it" or "this" or "card" are less directive.

Bookhandling Knowledge Task

WHO?

Developing readers.

WHY?

The **Bookhandling Knowledge Task** enables teachers to understand what young children know about specific literacy materials. Many young children have a surprising amount of information about how books are organized and the purposes for their use.

HOW?

The Bookhandling Knowledge Task is an adaptation of the work by Clay (1972) and Doake (1988). This form was created by Goodman, Altwerger, and Marek (1989) for research purposes, but also for teachers to use in the classroom with a variety of picture storybooks rather than only with the specific books that Clay developed. Administering the task is relatively simple: teacher and child sit side by side with a picture book. Teachers ask the questions and allow ample time for the child to respond. If possible, it's best to videotape the interview; otherwise, the interviewer or an adult observer should record in writing the child's responses.

WHAT ELSE?

Educators have a tendency to believe that once learners have knowledge about something in one context that they easily transfer it to other kinds of settings. Children often understand the role of print in books as different than the role of print in other environmental settings such as billboards, stores, food cartons and packages, or newspapers. Evaluating how children respond to print differently in different settings suggests that lots of experience with particular objects of literacy is necessary before teachers can expect children to be comfortable with the use of such materials. Teachers may want to discover how older students respond to magazines, TV guides, newspapers, encyclopedias, and other text by adapting the bookhandling knowledge accordingly.

— Adapted from Y. M. Goodman, B. Altwerger, and A. Marek. *Print Awareness in Preschool Children: The Development of Literacy in Preschool Children* (Occasional Paper no. 4, Program in Language and Literacy, College of Education, University of Arizona, 1989).

References

Clay, M. 1972. *The sand test.* Portsmouth, NH: Heinemann.
Doake, D. 1988. *Book experience and emergent reading in preschool children.* Vols. 1 and 2. Department of Elementary Education, University of Alberta, Canada.

See: INTERACTING pp. 102, 111, 116

Bookhandling Knowledge Task was developed by Yetta M. Goodman, professor of Reading, Language, and Culture at the School of Education, University of Arizona, Tucson.

Bookhandling Knowledge Task

Name _____ Date _____ Grade _____

Item	Administration	Instruction	Response	Child's Response
1	Show book; title covered by hand. Flip over pages	"What's this called?" "What's this thing?" If child answers with the name of the book, record and ask "What's (Name of book given by child)?"	"book" "story book" "story" name of book	
2	Displaying book	"What do you do with it?"	"read it" "look at it" "tell it" "open it"	
3	Displaying book	"What's inside it?"	"story" "picture" "words" "pages" "letters" "things"	
4	Present book wrong way up and back toward S	"Show me the front of this book" "Take the book and open it so that we can read it together	Any indication of front or first page	

(continued)

Item	Administration	Instruction	Possible Response	Child's Response
5	Turn to page 3	Hold on to a page and say "Show me a page in this book" "Is this a page?"	Points to page. "Yes"	
6	Give the book to child	"Read this to me."	Record all responses	
7	If child doesn't read the book or does inappropriate book reading, continue: Give the book to the child. Read the first page	"I'm going to read you this story. You show me where to start reading." "Where do I begin?"	Indicates print on first page	
8	Turn to next page	"Show me the top of this page." "Show me the bottom of this page."	Indicates top edge or toward top. Indicates bottom of page or toward bottom	

(continued)

Item	Administration	Instruction	Possible Response	Child's Response
9	Show the page to the child	"Show me with your finger exactly where I have to begin reading."	Points to the first word on the page	
10	Show the page to the child	"Show me with your finger which way I go as I read this page."	Left to right, on the page	
11	Continue to show the page to the child	"Where then?" (this may already have been done or stated in #9; if so, credit but do not repeat)	Top line to bottom line	
12	Read the page	"You point to the story while I read it." (Read slowly)	Exact matching of spoken word with written word. Close matching.	

(continued)

Item	Administration	Instruction	Possible Response	Child's Response
13	If there is print on both pages, display the pages	"Where do I go now?"	Points to the first line of print on the next page	
14	Read the next two pages. If possible, turn to a page with print and a picture on it. Turn the book upside down without the child seeing you.	"Can you or I read this now?" "Why or why not?"		
15	Show student how to use masking card to close the "curtains" over the "window." (Use two pieces of black cardboard)	"Let's put some of the story in this window. I want you to close the curtains like this until I can see just one letter." "Now just two letters."	One letter correct Two letters correct	
16	Open "curtains"	"Now close it until we can see just one word." "Now just two words."	One word correct Two words correct	

(continued)

Bookhandling Knowledge Task

Item	Administration	Instruction	Possible Response	Child's Response
17	Open "curtains"	"Show me the first letter in a word, any word"	First correct Last correct	
18	Remove card	"Show me a capital letter, any capital letter"	Points clearly to a capital letter. Points to any capital letter.	
19	Read to end of story Close book and pass it to the child	"Show me the name of the book" or "Name of story?"	Cover, fly-leaf, or title page	
20	Get at comprehension	"Tell me something about the story"		

(continued)

Item	Administration	Instruction	Possible Response	Child's Response
21	Leave the book with the child	"Show me the beginning of the story" "Show me the end of the story"	Opens book to first page and points to the first line. Turns to last page and points to the last line.	
22	Title page pointing	"It says here (read title of the book) by (read the author's name). What does by (author's name) mean?"	"He wrote it." "He made up the story." "He made the book."	

Child's Concepts of Reading · Child's Concepts of Written and Pictorial Representation

WHO?

Developing readers and writers.

WHY?

The knowledge a teacher gains from Interviews 1 and 2 helps teachers to organize a rich literacy curriculum in order to provide children with reading and writing experiences that become an important foundation for the reading and writing that goes on in school.

HOW?

INTERVIEW 1: **Child's Concepts of Reading.** Interview children to determine their concepts about and attitudes toward reading. The interview aids in understanding the perceptions young children have about the function of reading and the reading act itself. Interviewers should encourage as much discussion as possible in response to these questions.

INTERVIEW 2: **Child's Concepts of Written and Pictorial Representation.** This interview provides information regarding young children's concepts about writing as well as their use and understanding of print-oriented terminology. Children are asked to write and draw and then to react to their productions. The children should have available to them a variety of writing and drawing materials such as colored and white paper, lined and unlined paper, crayons, pencils, marking pens, etc. Teachers should note the degree to which the children's choice of materials varies according to the tasks.

WHAT ELSE?

Literacy is just another cultural artifact that young children notice and interact with, learning what it is, how it works, and what it means. Young children may understand that print "says something"; that it has directionality; that it comprises letters, words, and sentences; that it is different than drawing. Traditionally, however, schools have tended to ignore this knowledge, planning literacy instruction as though children are literacy neophytes. Interviews such as these help teachers discover what children do know about written language, and plan instruction that builds on children's rich knowledge.

— Adapted from Y. M. Goodman, B. Altwerger, and A. Marek. *Print awareness in preschool children: The development of literacy in preschool Children.* (Occasional Paper no. 4, Program in Language and Literacy, College of Education, University of Arizona, 1989).

See: INTERACTING pp. 102, 104

Child's Concepts of Reading and Child's Concepts of Written and Pictorial Representation were developed by Yetta M. Goodman, professor of Reading, Language, and Culture at the University of Arizona, Tucson.

Child's Concepts of Reading

Name _____ Date _____ Grade _____

Interviewer _____

1. Do you know how to read? _____
    If yes:
    a. How did you learn how to read?

    b. Did somebody help you to learn? _____   (if yes, who?)
       or, did you learn by yourself?

    c. Do you like to read?

    d. What do you like to read?

    If no:
    e. Do you want to be able to read?

    f. How will you learn to read?

    g. Does someone have to help you learn how to read?

    h. Who do you think will help you learn how to read?

2. Is it possible to learn to read by yourself?

3. Is learning to read easy/hard?

4. Why do you think learning to read is easy/hard?

5. Do the people you live with know how to read? _____
    If yes:
    a. What do they read?

    b. Where do they read? (kitchen, living room, etc.)

(continued)

6. Do the people you live with ever read to you? _____
   If yes:
   a. Who?

   b. What do they read?

   c. Do you like it?

   d. Why?

7. What do you look at while you are being read to? (Probe with "Anything else?")

8. a. If I said "I'm going to read you a story," what would I do?

   b. If I said "I'm going to tell you a story," what would I do?

   c. Are reading a story and telling a story the same or different? _____ How?

9. Can you read with your eyes closed? _____ How?

10. Do you have a TV? _____ Is there anything to read on TV?

11. Do you ever go to the store with your parents? _____
    If yes:
    a. Is there anything in the store that you read or people can read?

    b. What? (Try to get at books, magazines and newspapers, and labels
       without using those words. If not, ask directly about them.)

12. Why do people read?

13. Do you speak a language?

14. What do you speak?

Child's Concepts of Written and Pictorial Representation

Name _____ Date _____ Grade _____

Interviewer _____

1. a. Write for me. (If no response, say "Pretend to write for me.")

   b. Why did you choose those? (paper and writing implements)

2. a. Read me what you wrote.

   b. If child says "I can't," ask "Why not?" and then say "Pretend to read."

3. Tell me what you wrote. What are this and this? (Get at terms, words, letters, etc.)

4. Write me a letter.

5. a. What do you write at home?

   b. Do you write at school?

   c. What do you write at school?

6. What do you like to write?

7. Why do people write?

8. (Offer materials again)
   a. Draw me a picture.

   b. Why did you choose those?

(continued)

9. a. Show me your writing.

   b. Show me your drawing.

10. (Make sure child has samples of both his/her writing and drawing in front of him/her.)
    a. Is drawing the same as writing?

    b. How are they similar?

    c. How are they different?

11. Show child a variety of writing samples (manuscript, cursive, words written in languages other than English, a single letter, recurring letters, and non-writing samples such as simple drawings and geometric shapes). Ask child to identify which of the samples represent writing.

12. Write three different-looking names including the child's, and ask him/her to read his/her name and point to it.

Reading in Kindergarten

WHO?

Kindergarten students.

WHY?

Children arrive in kindergarten with varied experiences with reading and books. This poses an assessment problem, as each child needs to be assessed from his or her own starting point across a wide range of reading strategies. Denise Ogren's kindergarten children read on a regular basis with several adults—a Chapter 1 teacher, a reading specialist, and parents. She needs an assessment tool that serves all the children.

HOW?

Reading in Kindergarten is used with different books, so there is a space for the book title and a place to indicate whether the book is new to the child, somewhat familiar, or very familiar. The familiarity of the book makes a difference in the kindergarten child's ability to "read" it back to the adult, and also informs the listening adult that he or she may need to read the book first to the child before asking the child to read it back.

Basic knowledge about print, based on the work of Marie Clay (1972), is assessed next. Denise has included the exact words on the form that the adult reading assessors should use, because different adults use the form. A prediction question is included to ascertain the child's ability to predict story content. Since it would be too lengthy to record the entire answer, the assessor must use her own judgment to circle either "no response," "fair response," or "good response."

As the child reads, is he or she reading words that are similar to those in the book or is the child making up an entirely different story? Is the child paying attention to the meaning of the story? developing a reading vocabulary? What strategies can he or she use to find words in the story?

At the beginning of kindergarten most children only use the picture cues, or the pattern of the story, or they rely on their memory. As the year progresses, they begin to use graphophonic, syntactic, and semantic cues. There are a number of ways to assess comprehension. The child can retell the story, or the assessor can ask the child to relate the story to the child's experience.

WHAT ELSE?

This assessment tool serves as a record for the child's progress over the course of the school year. An adult needs to learn how to use the form and to understand the terminology and reasons for each question, but this takes a minimum of time.

Reference

Clay, M. 1972. *The sand test*. Portsmouth, NH: Heinemann.

See: MONITORING p. 9; OBSERVING p. 84; INTERACTING pp. 102, 104, 111

Reading in Kindergarten was developed by Denise Ogren, a kindergarten teacher at Stinesville Elementary School, Stinesville, IN.

Reading in Kindergarten

Child's Name _____ Date _____

Name of Adult _____

Name of Book _____

New book	☐ YES	☐ NO
Very familiar book	☐ YES	☐ NO
Somewhat familiar	☐ YES	☐ NO

"Where do you read?" Does child point to:

Words	☐ YES	☐ NO
Go left to right	☐ YES	☐ NO
Go top to bottom	☐ YES	☐ NO
Points word for word	☐ YES	☐ NO

"What do you think this book is about?" (Prediction/look at pictures):

☐ No response   ☐ Fair response   ☐ Good response

Reads words similar to those in book: ☐ YES   ☐ NO

"Do words and story always make sense?"   ☐ YES   ☐ NO

Can pick out an easy common noun in the story? List words.

"Find the word _____ for me?"   (Harder): "What does this word say?"

Child is able to:

Make corrections and predictions	☐ YES	☐ NO
Sound out more than initial sound only	☐ YES	☐ NO
Sound out initial letter of a word	☐ YES	☐ NO
Make good use of picture cues	☐ YES	☐ NO
Remember patterns in story	☐ YES	☐ NO
Self-correct for meaning	☐ YES	☐ NO
Use memory of the story	☐ YES	☐ NO

Retelling: to you, to another child

Uses book language	☐ YES	☐ NO
Proper sequence	☐ YES	☐ NO

Relates to self: "What did this book make you think of?" _____

_____

"Did you like this book?" _____ "Why?" _____

_____

☐ No response   ☐ Fair response   ☐ Good response

Classroom Community of Readers · Story Response

WHO?

Classroom Community of Readers works for elementary, middle school, and high school students. Story Response is intended for primary students.

WHY?

In Joan Ruddiman's reading workshop, one of the first mini-lessons she teaches has to do with the reader's responsibility and the responsibility an author has to the reader. She discusses the concept of abandoning a book: if after approximately fifty pages you are not "hooked," the author has not met his or her obligation to you, the reader. The reader invests the effort of reading those fifty pages to give the author a chance to set the scene, introduce characters, and get the plot rolling. She also discusses the understanding that not every book is for every reader. Readers make choices about what they read, as well as when, where, and how fast they read. This is the power readers have.

HOW?

To create this sense of power and community, all students complete at least one **Classroom Community of Readers** review per quarter. Students review books they have chosen to read themselves. The purpose of the reviews is to share impressions and interpretations as well as to recommend books the teacher and other students may enjoy. All reviews are posted on a classroom bulletin board so teachers and students can read them and begin to develop a sense of which books are the classroom favorites.

In a similar way, Avery Walker asks her first/second-grade students to complete a **Story Response** form. They are expected to research the meanings of any unknown words. The completed forms are shared verbally among small groups of students who have read the same book, sparking a literary dialogue.

WHAT ELSE?

Selecting books that work for us, that move and inform us, is an important aspect of reading, one that is often overlooked in school. As adults, we share and discuss our favorite reading choices with our friends, recommending or criticizing books we've encountered. We want to encourage a similar literary dialogue among our students.

See: REPORTING pp. 177, 181, 183

Classroom Community of Readers was developed by Joan Ruddiman, a teacher at West Windsor Plainsboro Middle School in Plainsboro, NJ.

Story Response was developed by Avery D. Walker, a first/second-grade teacher at Ohlone School in Palo Alto, CA.

Classroom Community of Readers

Name _____ Date _____

Title of book _____

Author _____

Number of pages _____

This book is ☐ fiction ☐ nonfiction

In five sentences, summarize the content of the book:

_____

_____

_____

_____

How do you rate this book?

☐ Fascinating ☐ Very interesting ☐ All right ☐ Dull ☐ Phooey

Tell why you rated the book as you did:

_____

_____

_____

_____

Signature of critic: _____

Story Response

Name _____ Date _____ Grade _____

Title of Book _____

Author _____

1. Predict how you think this story will end.

2. Did you like this story?

3. Did you like the illustrations?

4. I found some words that I did not know. Here are a few:

5. Make a list of the things that you liked about the story.

6. What was one thing that you did not like about the story?

7. Draw a picture of your favorite part of the story on the back.

Student Writing Survey/ Interest Inventory

WHO?

All students, K–8.

WHY?

Whole language teachers understand that it's easiest to write about things that you care about or know a lot about. They also believe that it is important for students to be reflective about their own writing process and to understand the connection between reading and writing. The **Student Writing Survey/Interest Inventory** helps students reflect on writing and, at the same time, identifies topics they might want to explore in writing or through research. The information is invaluable for teachers in planning supportive instruction and creating stimulating curriculum that addresses the needs and interests of their students.

HOW?

Older students can complete the form on their own; teachers interview younger students or ask parents or older students to assist if teachers can't take the time themselves.

WHAT ELSE?

It may be helpful for students to complete the inventory at least twice a year, and then compare the results—how have their interests changed? What do they know about the writing process later in the school year that they didn't know at the start?

See: MONITORING pp. 28, 30, 32; INTERACTING p. 99

Student Writing Survey was developed by Maureen White, K–8 writing coordinator for Haverhill Public Schools in Haverhill, MA.

Student Writing Survey/Interest Inventory

Name _____ Date _____ Grade _____

1. Do you like to write? Why, or why not?

2. Why do people write?

3. What makes a piece of writing effective?

4. What do you do especially well?

5. What are your favorite books?

6. What are you most curious about (what would you like to learn about)?

Peer Conferencing ·
Peer Conferencing Guidelines ·
Help the Author

WHO?

Elementary through secondary-level students.

WHY?

In whole language classrooms, teachers attempt to meet in small-group or individual conferences with every student at least once a week. In addition, students conference with each other in peer conferences. The **Peer Conferencing** sheet, **Peer Conferencing Guidelines**, and **Help the Author** provide students with guidelines for successful peer conferencing. The forms also help students keep track of the peers with whom they've conferenced, the pieces on which they've conferenced, and what decisions were made regarding the evolution of their writing. Conferences are most effective when students leave the conference with a clear plan about what they will do next with their writing.

HOW?

There are many ways to organize for peer conferences. Some teachers allow students to arrange a peer conference whenever students feel a need. Other teachers restrict peer conferences somewhat. They may allow a limited number to take place at any given time. For instance, students may meet in designated conferencing areas only. If all areas are occupied, they have to wait until an area becomes available. Other teachers monitor the time students can spend peer conferencing, setting a time limit of ten or fifteen minutes.

WHAT ELSE?

Some teachers might prefer to keep the conference forms in their own files; others might allow students to keep them in their writing folders. Still others may photocopy the forms so both they and their students have copies.

See: MONITORING pp. 28, 30, 32; ANALYZING p. 166

Peer Conferencing and Peer Conferencing Guidelines were developed by Maureen White, K–8 writing coordinator for Haverhill Public Schools in Haverhill, MA.

Help the Author was developed by teachers in Palo Alto Unified School District in Palo Alto, CA.

Peer Conferencing

Name _____

DATE	TOPIC	PARTNER	SUGGESTIONS

Peer Conferencing Guidelines

SPEAK IN QUIET VOICES DURING PEER CONFERENCING. OTHER WRITERS MAY BE DRAFTING, AND IT'S HARD TO THINK WHEN YOUR THOUGHTS ARE INTERRUPTED.

WRITER

1. SHARE YOUR WORK WITH ANOTHER WRITER. Each person must read his/her own piece to the listener. She/he may want to ask the listener for help on a particular aspect of the piece, such as "Let me know if I've been less wordy this time."

2. LISTEN CAREFULLY TO THE COMMENTS OF THE LISTENER. You may take notes on the suggestions to consider using them.

3. DECIDE HOW OR IF TO USE THE CONFERENCING SUGGESTIONS. Remember, the purpose of conferencing is to lead the writer directly to revising (adding, deleting, changing) her/his text.

LISTENER

1. LOOK AND LISTEN TO THE WRITER WHO IS SHARING. The listener should listen carefully and take notes so that she/he can point out places in the piece where she/he had thought the writing worked well. She/he may ask the writer to repeat a part, read more slowly, loudly, etc.

2. TELL THE WRITER WHAT YOU HEARD. TELL THE WRITER A DETAIL THAT YOU LIKED ABOUT THE TEXT. Be sure to use specific details, such as "I enjoyed the description of your school's locker room as pungent with the odor of old sweat socks."

3. SAY TO THE WRITER, "TELL ME MORE ABOUT..." OR "WHAT DO YOU MEAN BY...?" OR "I'M CONFUSED BY..." Feel free to ask the writer any questions about his/her piece.

4. AVOID TELLING THE AUTHOR WHAT TO DO. Do not tell the author what to do with her/his piece. Avoid the words "You should." Remember, do not take away the writer's ownership.

SUPPORT EACH OTHER BY SHARING YOUR STRATEGIES

Help the Author

Your Name: _____

Author's Name: _____

Title of paper discussed: _____

DIRECTIONS: Choose a partner with whom to share your writing. As you complete each part of this worksheet be sure to check it off in the DONE column.

DONE	ACTIVITY
	1. Author reads her/his paper out loud to you.
	2. You read author's paper out loud to him/her. As you read the paper, watch how the author develops his/her ideas.
	3. Find a sentence you especially like ("the golden line") and underline it. Explain to the author why you like this sentence.
	4. What compliment (+) can you give the author about this writing? What suggestion can you make to the author for making this writing even better (–)? Summarize here:
	5. *If the author agrees, copy the golden line on a large piece of paper.

Sub-table for activity 4:

+	–

Now repeat the process with your piece of writing.

* optional

Parent-Student Questionnaire · Getting to Know Your Child

WHO?

All whole language teachers, students, and parents.

WHY?

Communicating with parents is an important aspect of all whole language programs, especially with respect to assessment and evaluation. Parents must understand the philosophy underlying the program, the curriculum as it is translated into classroom practice, and the system of assessment and evaluation. And teachers must understand their students, their home experiences, and their parents' expectations for their education. Forms such as **Parent-Student Questionnaire** and **Getting to Know Your Child** open and support an invaluable home-school dialogue.

HOW?

We can ask parents to become partners in the evaluation of their children's progress in several ways:

- We can ask them what goals they have for their children.
- We can ask them to observe their children to assist us in understanding the home and community environments. Specific ways of observing should be communicated to parents early in the year.
- We can invite them to parent-teacher-child conferences as we discuss together our mutual goals for their children, our progress toward these goals, and our plans for the future. Children are often very knowledgeable about their own capabilities and progress, and where the atmosphere is open and non-threatening, they are willing to comment about themselves.
- We can negotiate with parents by informing them about our reporting procedures and asking them what kind of information they would like to have. A letter can be sent home prior to reporting time that details different possibilities and asks whether or not parents would like an in-depth analysis for any part of the curriculum.

WHAT ELSE?

When we consider assessment and evaluation as separate from instruction, the time required seems almost impossible! However, when we realize that the processes of teaching, learning, communicating with parents, and assessment and evaluation are not linear but are recursive and are part of everything we do on an ongoing basis, the lines of demarcation disappear and the educational experience of the child becomes integrated and holistic.

See: REPORTING p. 231

Parent-Student Questionnaire was developed by Norma I. Mickelson, professor emeritus of the University of Victoria, British Columbia, Canada.

Getting to Know Your Child was developed by Catherine P. Howard, third/fourth-grade teacher at Ohlone School in Palo Alto, CA.

Parent-Student Questionnaire

Name _____ Date _____ Grade _____

Teacher _____

The most useful responses are those that are specific. Please (parents and children) fill out the following:

1. Has the teacher been available to talk with you and been responsive to your concerns this year?

   Parent response:

   Child response:

2. What is going well for your child this year?

   Parent response:

   Child response:

3. In what ways do you feel you / your child is making progress?

   Parent response:

   Child response:

(continued)

4. What concerns (if any) do you have?

   Parent response:

   Child response:

5. What suggestions do you have?

   Parent response:

   Child response:

6. What questions do you have?

   Parent response:

   Child response:

7. Please add any additional comments:

   Parent response:

   Child response:

Date: _____ Parent Signature(s) _____
        (Your signatures are optional, but in order to respond we need to know who you are.)

Getting to Know Your Child

Dear parents:

This information is most helpful to me as I get to know your child and you. Please send it at your earliest convenience. Thank you.

Use the back, if needed.

1. What changes (health, maturity, interests) have occurred in the life of your child this summer?

2. What areas of school life has your child especially enjoyed?

3. Toward what areas of school life has your child expressed negative or ambivalent feelings?

4. In general, how is your child's self-concept? Does he/she believe in his/her abilities?

5. What special needs (academic, social, personal) does your child have?

6. What goals do you have for your child this year?

7. Where does your child go after school?

8. What are favorite after-school or weekend interests and activities?

9. What else do you want me to know about your child or about you?

From _____   Date _____

Principal's Goals for the School/Classroom

WHO?

These guidelines are appropriate for all whole language teachers and principals.

WHY?

Whole language is a philosophy of teaching rather than a method or collection of activities. This belief has guided Bob Wortman's decision-making and interactions in supporting the professional growth of the Borton Elementary School staff. Each classroom reflects the individual strengths and interests of teachers.

HOW?

As teachers must become more deliberate and reflective in their teaching, Bob expects them to have very specific goals for their classrooms that take into account their teaching philosophies and belief systems, their knowledge of learning theory and child development, their classroom as social entities, the needs of individual students, and their professional growth needs. **Principal's Goals for the School** and **Principal's Goals for the Classroom** reflect his beliefs about learning and teaching.

OBSERVATION. He tries to accomplish walk-throughs in the school each day. He also schedules time in the classrooms regularly to read to or with the children. He rotates his classroom visits from week to week in order to spread his presence equally among all the children, and keeps anecdotal records of his classroom visitations. Teachers may formally request that he evaluate a specific lesson, but in general they prefer to be evaluated informally.

CONFERENCING. Bob sets up two formal individual conferences with teachers each year. During the first conference, Bob discusses professional goals set by the teacher from the previous May and identifies resources needed to meet those goals. Next they go through the teacher's class list and discuss each child.

The second formal evaluation is formally documented as the summative evaluation for district and consensus purposes. Bob shares the anecdotal records that have been collected over the year as well as parents' notes of praise and classroom newsletters that reflect strengths. They discuss the goals set for the year and negotiate the goals for the following year. Bob also encourages the teachers to write self-evaluative statements concerning their own learning and validating their professional growth.

WHAT ELSE?

Bob sees the positive results in the curriculum and in the faces of children when teachers are allowed to build on their strengths and to choose and monitor the changes in their own practice. In this way, he is not just an overseer of a school, but a fully participating member of a learning community.

See: INTERACTING p. 138; OBSERVING p. 90; REPORTING p. 214

Principal's Goals for the School and Principal's Goals for the Classroom were developed by Robert C. Wortman, principal of Borton Elementary School, Tucson, AZ.

Principal's Goals for the School

_____ SAFE SOCIAL AND EMOTIONAL CLIMATE FOR STAFF AS WELL AS STUDENTS. Staff members should feel comfortable coming to work each day, knowing that everyone is a valued member of the community.

_____ RESPECTFUL AND SUPPORTIVE ENVIRONMENT. Teachers have the professional autonomy to make informed decisions without fear of being redressed in public by the principal or peers. There must be agreement on the need for disagreement in a healthy community.

_____ RISK-TAKING AND PERMISSION TO FAIL. It must be understood at all times that innovation and creativity are valued in the school community. To be creative, teachers must feel safe to try out new ideas and techniques.

_____ COLLABORATIVE COMMUNITY. Teachers must work and plan together if they are to learn and grow professionally. Time and resources must be provided for the staff to find the time to meet and plan together.

_____ FUN. The sign of a healthy community is the degree to which the individuals enjoy one another's company and enjoy being in the workplace. People that have fun together are less likely to denigrate one another.

_____ FOCUS ON LEARNING RATHER THAN ON TEACHING. A teacher can "teach" a concept over and over, but if the student isn't understanding, then learning isn't taking place. The teacher must be able to assess the prior knowledge of the students in order to make the deliberate teaching decisions that best facilitate learning.

_____ THE SCHOOL AS A SCHOLARLY, ACADEMIC COMMUNITY. Teachers should be able to articulate their beliefs and professional decisions about teaching and learning to parents, administrators, and peers.

_____ STRONG HOME-SCHOOL CONNECTION. Parents must feel welcome in their school at all times. Schools need to feel more accessible to all parents by being less formal and restrictive.

_____ STRENGTHEN THE SCHOOL'S PUBLIC IMAGE. The principal is in the primary position to promote the interests of the school and represent the strengths of the school and staff members in the public eye. The principal needs to take every opportunity in the community and at professional conferences to spotlight teachers and programs.

Principal's Goals for the Classroom

_____ OWNERSHIP BY THE CHILDREN. All children should have their work displayed—not just their "best" but their real work. Bulletin boards and displays should be created by kids for their own purposes.

_____ CONTENT-RICH. A walk through the classroom should reveal the thematic unit the children are studying. The text sets and displayed works of kids should reflect science, math, social studies, or fine arts themes.

_____ AESTHETICS OF THE ENVIRONMENT. The children's work should be displayed beautifully and with pride. Plants, art prints, and striking displays of children's artwork make powerful visual statements and help children develop a sense of audience in new contexts.

_____ SOCIAL/EMOTIONAL CLIMATE. The parameters for living and working together are discussed. The norms for the classroom are posted so that the teacher can assist kids in focusing on the social necessity for maintaining a supportive and positive environment. The interactions among students and teacher should reflect the agreed-upon goals of the classroom.

_____ LITERATE ENVIRONMENT. A variety of print resources are available to students at all times.

HOPS: A Holistic Observation Process

WHO?

All whole language schools, teachers, principals, and curriculum leaders.

WHY?

The **Holistic Observation Process (HOPS)** is an informal professional evaluation tool designed for principals or other supervisors. Unlike the traditional clinical supervision model, HOPS is aligned with holistic literacy instruction. It is an evaluation process that whole language teachers will look forward to, not just tolerate, because it creates opportunities for teachers and principals to explore and examine teaching and learning together.

HOW?

HOPS contains the following elements: the **Pre-Observation Conference**, **Classroom Observation**, **Written Feedback**, and a post-observation conference (for example, see Post-Conference Evaluation, page 238). The difference between it and a traditional model is that the administrator focuses on the students during the classroom observation. The administrator serves to empower teachers, inviting them to examine and reflect on their own teaching in order to become their own instructional leaders. In this way, administrators form positive, working relationships with teachers and encourage them to grow as professionals.

WHAT ELSE?

David Crabtree, principal of Wamsley Elementary School in Rifle, Colorado, who has piloted HOPS, admits that it takes more time than the traditional clinical supervision. However, he reports that the extended observation "provides an opportunity to get a more realistic and accurate view of the classroom atmosphere." Also, "teachers love to talk about their classrooms and their kids. It provides them with an opportunity to have someone listen to their philosophy, methods, routines, etc. They appreciate the feedback they receive, especially the comments from the students. And, they find the process less threatening and more growth oriented." Another somewhat unexpected advantage is the impact HOPS has on the students. Crabtree has found that since he started using HOPS, he spends more time in the classrooms interacting with students. The end result? Students seek him out on the playground to report that they are following his suggestion that they take books home each night to read to their parents. Another bonus: he is receiving more letters than ever before from students.

— Adapted from "HOPS: A Holistic Observation Process for Supervising Whole Language Teachers and Classrooms" (*Colorado Reading Council Journal*, Spring 1992, pp. 9–13).

See: OBSERVING p. 90; REPORTING pp. 214, 238

The HOPS model was developed by Yvonne Siu-Runyan, an associate professor at the University of Northern Colorado, and Janice V. Kristo, associate professor at the University of Maine, Orono.

HOPS: Pre-Observation Conference

The following questions and comments will help the supervisor learn about the classroom, become a knowledgeable observer, and most important, develop and nurture a professional, collegial, collaborative relationship with teachers.

THE LITERATE ENVIRONMENT:

1. Take me on a tour of your classroom and describe it so that I can better understand the learning environment you have created.

2. Tell me what a typical day is like in your classroom.

3. Tell me about the ways you integrate reading and writing across the curriculum.

4. What are the parents' comments about your reading and writing program?

5. Tell me what is going well in your classroom. What are you struggling with?

THE GROWING PROFESSIONAL:

6. What kinds of professional readings are you doing lately? What about reading for enjoyment?

7. Are you doing any writing? Talk to me about that.

8. What are you thinking about in relation to reading and writing these days? Have you revised your thinking about reading and writing in any way?

9. What would you like me to notice in your classroom? Why?

LEARNING FROM STUDENTS:

10. Any particular questions you would like me to ask your students? Why?

11. Is there anything you would like me to do with your students while I am in your classroom? Why?

12. Would you mind if I ask students _____ while I am in you classroom? I would like to do so because _____ .

HOPS: Classroom Observation

Supervisors may select only a sampling of the following questions to ask several students, or they may ask the same question(s) of all of them. The point is to experiment, to try out the questions, and learn what works best. Another possibility is to have the teacher choose questions. The teacher may help in collecting information she believes is important.

1. Take me on a tour of your classroom so I can learn about what goes on in the different areas, such as the library, writing center, reading corner, learning center, etc.

2. Describe your classroom to me. Tell me what a typical day is like. What are some things I should notice about what happens in your classroom?

3. How much time do you spend reading and writing everyday?

4. What are you working on in your writing? What are you reading?

5. What do you like best about reading and writing?

6. What are some of your favorite books?

7. Does your teacher share her reading and writing with the class? What do you think about that?

Talk with students and observe them doing literate activities to learn about their understanding of reading and writing.

1. What are you good at in reading? Why? What about writing?

2. What do you want to get better at in your reading? What about your writing?

3. When you get stuck in reading or writing, what do you do? Why?

4. What have you learned recently about reading? What about writing?

Have a student read aloud and notice the strategies s/he uses.
-   Does the reader integrate the use of semantic cues (meaning), syntactic cues (structural or grammatical cues), graphophonic cues (sound-symbol relationships), and schematic cues (background knowledge)? Or, does the reader rely only on one to the exclusion of the others?
-   What kinds of miscues (unexpected response to the text) does the student make? Are they ones that make sense or do they detract from making meaning?
-   Notice the kinds of conversations students are having about their reading. Do they talk about the meaning of the piece? Or are they overly concerned with oral reading?
-   Notice the kinds of conversations student are having about their writing. Are they using the writing process? Or are they overly concerned with mechanics and spelling during the drafting stage?
-   Are students writing on self-selected topics? Or are they all writing about a topic selected by the teacher?
-   Are students conferencing with one another as they write?

1. Would you share your writing folder with me? Show me a piece you are most proud of this year. Why? What piece do you consider to be not very good? Why?

2. How do you go about choosing a topic for writing?

HOPS: Written Feedback

Consider the following criteria as a guide when reflecting on the student' comments. If the teacher asks or wants to do some self-evaluation, then this set of guidelines may be helpful.

THE CLASSROOM AS A LITERATE COMMUNITY:

1. How is time used and how has the teacher helped the students take responsibility for how they use time?

2. Do students use reading and writing for authentic reasons?

3. Do the students enjoy reading and writing or do they see them as chores?

4. What is the teacher's role in the classroom? Does the teacher share her own reading and writing with the class? Is the teacher part of the community of readers and writers?

THE STUDENTS' UNDERSTANDING OF READING AND WRITING:

1. Do the students understand that reading is for understanding and not word-calling?

2. Do the students understand that writing is for communicating ideas and not just using standard spelling, punctuation, and grammar? Do the students understand that there is a process they can use to get from ideas to a final copy?

3. Are the students flexible in the strategies they use for inquiring into unknown words? Or are they relying mostly on one strategy?

4. Do students offer one another helpful suggestions when conferencing with one another about their writing? This shows what they have learned.

5. What are some of the things students are struggling with?

Language Arts Review

WHO?

All faculty members.

WHY?

The **Language Arts Review** enables teachers to think about and evaluate their school's language arts program. Teachers are invited to consider what is working well about the program and what needs work.

HOW?

Teachers can fill the form out on their own, or members of a language arts committee can interview their colleagues. The responses should be summarized, tabulated, and shared with the entire faculty. Together, they can plot the course of change toward a more effective language arts program.

WHAT ELSE?

The form should be adapted to assess other aspects of a school's curriculum. After all, the art of teaching is self-reflection, evaluation, and continual revision. In this way, faculty rooms come alive with an intercollegial hum as teachers reflect on, debate, and revise, like artists and scientists, the evolving work in their classroom laboratories. They are reflective practitioners within a school community of thinkers and learners.

See: INTERACTING p. 131

Language Arts Review was developed by an unknown author.

Language Arts Review

Staff Member's Name _____ Date _____

Position _____ Interviewer _____

1. What do you see as the big issues and concerns relative to language arts in this school?

2. What do you think are the major strengths of the current language arts program?

3. What do you think are some of the current program's major weaknesses?

4. What are you doing to assist students who come from a non-English-speaking background to develop oral and written language competency in English?

5. What are you doing to celebrte and maintain the students' home language(s)?

6. How do you think language arts instruction could be improved within this school, i.e., what changes would you make?

(continued)

7. What changes have you thought about making...?
   Classroom Teachers ...in your classroom?
   Special Teachers   ...in your special program?
   Principal   ...in the school?
   Aides   ...in how you're currently working with the students?

   What prevents you from making such changes?

8. What things have you currently done to update yourself professionally in the language arts?

9. What aspects of the language arts do you feel most comfortable with?

10. What aspects do you feel least comfortable with?

11. What kinds of support or training do you wish you had available to you?

12. Is the school's language arts curriculum guide followed?

   If yes: How do you use it?
            How do you think it could be made more useful?

   If no: Why do you think it isn't being followed?
            How do you think it could be made more useful?

13. What else do you think we should know in order to understand things more fully?

Oral Language Evaluation

WHO?

Kindergarten through secondary students.

WHY?

Teachers can evaluate their students' oral language development and determine whether the classroom is providing opportunities for students to communicate. The **Oral Language Evaluation** form provides insight into the oral fluency each student is developing in a variety of classroom situations.

HOW?

The evaluation guidelines include observations related to students' flexibility, attitudes, and knowledge about language. The items should not be viewed as all-encompassing; they should be altered to suit each teacher's purposes.

WHAT ELSE?

Oral language, as students' primary means of learning about the world, is a valuable resource that demands to be developed and used in classrooms as well as at home. Teachers will want to develop strategies for fostering, supporting, and assessing oral language development across linguistic contexts at school. Regarding the assessment of student talk, Curt Dudley-Marling and Dennis Searle (1991) argue persuasively that "linguistic form is important only insofar as it affects function"; in other words, since the "purpose of language is communication, the effectiveness of a person's language can only be determined by examining its effect on the audience." The overarching question, then, becomes: "Does [the talk] work? If it doesn't work, then we can ask why."

— Adapted from Tucson TAWL, *A Kidwatching Guide: Evaluation for Whole Language Classrooms* (Occasional Paper no. 9, Program in Language and Literacy, College of Education, University of Arizona, Tucson, January 1984).

Reference

Dudley-Marling, C., and Searle, D. 1991. *When students have time to talk*. Portsmouth, NH: Heinemann.

See: REPORTING pp. 210, 231

Oral Language Evaluation was developed by Tucson TAWL members Ann Marek, Don Howard, Jane Disinger, Debra Jacobson, N. Earle, Yetta M. Goodman, Wendy Hood, Carol Woodley, John Woodley, Jackie Wortman, and Bob Wortman.

Oral Language Evaluation

1. Observation of communication in different-size groupings:
   a. one-to-one with adult
   b. one-to-one with peer
   c. small self-chosen peer group
   d. small instructional group
   e. whole group
   f. adapts to change in setting.

2. Observation of student's different language functions
   a. can tell a story
   b. can retell events
   c. can explain how to do or make something
   d. can talk on a variety of topics
   e. can give elaborated responses to teacher's questions.

3. Observation of interactional competencies:
   a. can ask teacher questions for assistance
   b. can ask peers questions for assistance
   c. initiates conversation
   d. when talking, holds the attention of others
   e. builds meaningfully on others' utterances
   f. uses social skills, e.g., appropriate turn-taking; can maintain or terminate a conversation; appropriate responses
   g. uses appropriate nonverbal behavior, e.g., gestures, facial expression, posture, indications s/he is listening, etc.
   h. shows awareness of listener needs, e.g., recycles, repairs, clarifies.

4. Observation of interactive form of oral language:
   a. uses comprehensible speech
   b. uses adequate one-word or clause responses to questions
   c. elaborates coherently on "instructional" topics.

Assessing the Spelling Levels of Young Children

WHO?

Developing writers from preschool through second grade.

WHY?

Young, developing writers who are forced to spell in a conventional way may become confused and obstructed from developing naturally. Therefore, the formal teaching of spelling with weekly spelling tests has no place in a curriculum for young children. Whole language teachers accept young children's early spelling with the understanding that children will acquire more conventionalized spelling as they experience authentic written language in a community of readers and writers.

HOW?

By following the suggestions in **Assessing the Spelling Levels of Young Children**, a teacher can easily assess spelling development. The Mannings' spelling study (Kamii, Long, Manning, and Manning, 1990), based on the spelling research of Ferreiro and Teberosky (1982) with English-speaking children, found six developmental levels.

WHAT ELSE?

Some teachers have found it helpful to send this form home at the beginning of the school year with an explanation of developmental spelling for parents. In this way, parents can become aware of, appreciate, and follow their own child's developmental process, understanding that that child's orthographic experimentation evolves into conventional spelling.

References

Ferreiro, E., and Teberosky, A. 1982. *Literacy before schooling*. Portsmouth, NH: Heinemann. (Original work published 1979.)

Kamii, C., Long, R., Manning, M., and Manning, G. 1990. Spelling in kindergarten: A constructivist analysis comparing Spanish-speaking and English-speaking children. *Journal of Research in Education*, 4, 91–97.

See: MONITORING p. 35

Assessing the Spelling Levels of Young Children was developed by Maryann and Gary Manning, professors at the University of Alabama, Birmingham.

Assessing the Spelling Levels of Young Children

LEVEL 0: Children draw pictures or scribble rather than make letters or symbol-like forms.

LEVEL 1: Children write a string of letters for a word that has no set number of letters from one word to another. The string might fill an entire page as a child spells a word.

ELOWr	= punishment
FROLMrH	= cement
LOErHt	= vacation
RIWrHtE	= motion
tWLHEtr	= ocean
FLJDErAtW	= taco
RLCErHDWt	= karate
LDErCWtRAHBT	= tomato

LEVEL 2: Children write a string of letters that usually consists of three to six letters for each word. The letters may be different for each word or the same letters might be rearranged from one word to the next.

hbR	= punishment
bRC	= cement
Bor	= vacation
RoL	= motion
LSWN	= ocean
SNVh	= taco
FMJO	= karate
MEJ	= tomato

LEVEL 3: Children at this level, the consonantal level, make letter-sound correspondences, using mostly consonants and letter-name vowels. For example, they may write SMT for cement.

PNMt	= punishment
SMt	= cement
VKN	= vacation
MLN	= motion
OSN	= ocean
TKO	= taco
KRt	= karate
TMT	= tomato

LEVEL 4: Children at this level, the alphabetic level, make letter-sound correspondences using consonants and vowels. For instance, they might write VACASHUN for vacation or MOSHUN for motion. These consistencies suggest the construction of a system approaching conventional spelling.

Punishmet	= punishment
Moashun	= motion
VayKayshTion	= vacation
Seament	= cement
Ocen	= ocean
Tacoa	= taco
Karaty	= karate
Tamaytoa	= tomato

LEVEL 5: Children spell most words in the conventional way.

Development of Narrative/ Expository · Reading Strategies · Conventions of Print

WHO?

Kindergarten through fifth grade.

WHY?

The teachers at Horace Mann School moved toward portfolio evaluation after experiencing the frustration shared by teachers in meaning-based, child-centered programs. They were convinced that their students knew more than skills-based standardized tests were telling them.

HOW?

Michael Hagan explains: "As often as possible, we want one sample of student work to document several areas. For example, the rough draft of a story might demonstrate current understanding of spelling, use of narrative voice, and legibility of printing. As items are added to the portfolio, others are removed and sent home. At the end of the year, only a handful are selected to represent progress to date. We also include the **Development of Narrative/Expository** in the portfolio to document the written language growth we've noted in each student.

"A manageable system is selective. We need to document those items that will accurately, if not completely, portray a child's emerging control of literacy. We defined a dozen strategies that fluent readers use almost unconsciously. As a child demonstrates consistent use of a particular strategy, the current teacher initials and dates on the left side of the **Reading Strategies** form. The teacher also includes running records, miscue analysis, notes, or commentary to document the child's use of the strategy. In addition, the teacher notes the child's growing self-awareness of his or her own reading strategies. We list twenty-seven print conventions on our **Conventions of Print** form. They are seen as indicators of growing control of literacy, not as determiners of grade-level achievement. Progress is individual, not sequential.

WHAT ELSE?

"Our portfolio is meant to be reflective of what a learner knows. My job as a classroom teacher is to identify learner strengths upon which to build. The three forms for language arts remain with a child from kindergarten through fifth grade. There is no timetable established for any child to complete a specific number of objectives in any given year. Teacher observations and notes might explain a child's progress (or lack of the same), providing insights into this learner. Sharing the same goals, we can build upon the work of colleagues."

See: OBSERVING pp. 84, 93

Development of Narrative/Expository, Reading Strategies, and Conventions of Print were developed by Michael Hagan and his colleagues at Horace Mann School in San Jose, CA.

Development of Narrative / Expository

Name _____

Grade _____

NARRATIVE

DATE/
OBSERVER

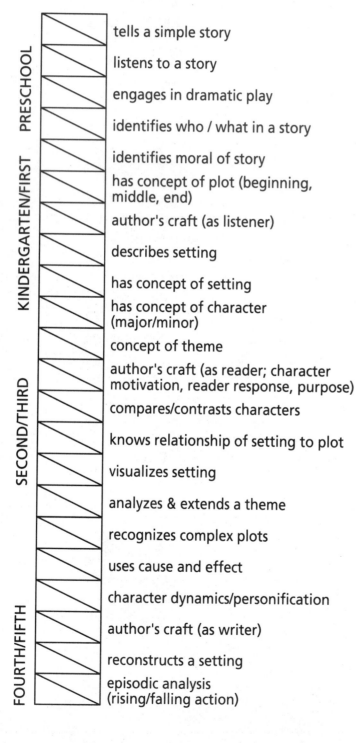

- tells a simple story
- listens to a story
- engages in dramatic play
- identifies who / what in a story
- identifies moral of story
- has concept of plot (beginning, middle, end)
- author's craft (as listener)
- describes setting
- has concept of setting
- has concept of character (major/minor)
- concept of theme
- author's craft (as reader; character motivation, reader response, purpose)
- compares/contrasts characters
- knows relationship of setting to plot
- visualizes setting
- analyzes & extends a theme
- recognizes complex plots
- uses cause and effect
- character dynamics/personification
- author's craft (as writer)
- reconstructs a setting
- episodic analysis (rising/falling action)

PRESCHOOL

KINDERGARTEN/FIRST

SECOND/THIRD

FOURTH/FIFTH

EXPOSITORY

DATE/
OBSERVER

- takes part in large group investigation
- creates a picture that informs
- differentiates between fiction/non-fiction

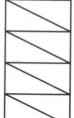

- presents an informative piece
- uses a variety of sources
- uses conventions (table of contents, title page, bibliography)
- finds author's voice

- understands appropriate resource & format
- organizes & interprets information
- understands forms of expository
- identifies author's purpose

Reading Strategies

Name _____   Grade _____

Date	Observer	(A strategy is self-assessed when a child is aware of using it.)	Self-Assessed
		Reading is supposed to make sense. Think about that before you read. When something doesn't make sense, you need to stop and find out why.	
		Think about what you already know about the topic. You probably know some of the things the author knows.	
		Try to predict what will happen next. Do this often while reading. Check your predictions now and then to see if they were right.	
		Skip words that you don't know or can't sound out. You don't need to read every word to know what's happening.	
		Think about the context. What you've read so far, or will be reading in the next few sentences, may provide needed information.	
		Look at the pictures for information. Pictures are there to provide information, sometimes in ways that words can't.	
		When something doesn't make sense, go back and read it again. Learn how to fix your own mistakes.	
		Reading is just like talking. Think about the way English works. (for example, "I went to the ____." needs a noun.)	
		Try to read several words together sometimes, like "Once upon a time."	
		Sound it out. Think about what you know about letter names and sounds.	
		Read different things different ways. Sometimes readers skip through a piece, sometimes they read from the beginning. Use the table of contents and index.	
		Try to imagine what the character or the place looks like. Try to make a movie in your head.	

Conventions of Print

Name _____

Date _____

Grade _____

PRINT AWARENESS

knows letter names				
knows letter sounds				
recognizes/uses space between words				
understands letter-to-letter/word-to-word correspondence				
reads left to right/top to bottom				

SPELLING

uses pretend spelling (scribbling, strings of letters)				
uses temporary spelling with initial and final consonants				
temporary spelling easily read				
uses temporary spelling with vowels				
high frequency words show standard spelling				
most words show standard spelling				

PUNCTUATION AND CAPITALIZATION

uses proper punctuation at end of each sentence				
uses capital "I" and capitals on proper names				
uses capitals at beginning of each sentence				
uses proper punctuation				

GRAMMAR

uses complete sentences											
knows rhyming words											
knows opposites											
uses proper word order in sentences											
knows/uses singular/plural											
knows/uses correct verb tense											
knows contractions											
knows root words											
knows prefixes/suffixes											
identifies parts of speech											
uses a variety of sentence structures											
uses paragraph structure											

Developing a Reading Profile

WHO? ———————————————————————————

Appropriate for all readers, with some adaptation for young developing readers.

WHY? ———————————————————————————

Becoming a reader is a complex, subtle process. Discovering how students are responding to reading is best accomplished by exploring a variety of data: their written responses to what they are reading, their talk about books and authors, retellings of stories they've read, awareness of their own reading strategies, and so forth.

HOW? ———————————————————————————

As Debra Goodman reads through her students' literature logs, she uses **Developing a Reading Profile** to create a reading portrait of each student. Answers to these questions coupled with miscue data collected during informal teacher-student reading conferences provide Debra with detailed and specific information about her students as readers.

WHAT ELSE? ———————————————————————————

Observing children as they make their way around and through books reveals far more about their propensity for reading than traditional measures of reading ability. Whole language teachers, like Debra Goodman, often engage their students in conversations about reading: What is it? Why do people read? Why do you read? What do you like to read? What do you experience as you are reading? Reading is not a precise process of word identification; it is the creation of a new world of meaning—one shaped by both the author and the reader. To understand our students as readers, we must examine the multiple dimensions of their reading experiences.

See: OBSERVING p. 69

Developing a Reading Profile was developed by Debra Goodman, who teaches fifth grade at the Dewey Learning Center in Detroit, MI.

Developing a Reading Profile

1. How much reading is the reader doing?

2. Is the reader having trouble finding books to read?

3. Is the reader sampling different genre?

4. What kinds of books is the reader interested in?

5. What books is the reader able to read on his or her own?

6. How does the reader choose to share the books with others?

7. Is the reader able to communicate in writing?

8. Does the reader give opinions in his or her reading log?

   Are the opinions supported with examples or details?

9. Does the log indicate that the reader is understanding the texts he or she is reading?

10. Does the reader give a synopsis or summary of the text?

11. Does the reader relate to characters in the story?

12. Does the reader analyze the text or the author's writing style?

Miscue Analysis: Forms and Procedures

WHO?

All readers.

WHY?

A miscue is an unexpected response to a written text. By analyzing the miscues students make as they read out loud, teachers can learn how their students use the four language systems (graphophonics, syntax, semantics, and pragmatics) and various reading strategies (sampling, predicting, confirming) to construct meaning.

HOW?

Teachers who use miscue analysis must be knowledgeable about its rationale and purposes in order to interpret the information with sufficient understanding. (For more information about miscue analysis, consult the reference list below.) **General Procedure for Marking Miscues** explains how to identify and mark the different types of miscues. The **Miscue Analysis Procedure III Questions** are used to ask questions about each sentence with miscues marked on a complete transcript of a story or article. No tape recording is necessary of the student's oral reading for Procedure IV. **Miscue Analysis Procedure IV Individual Conference Form** is used in a reading conference setting. Both forms help teachers organize the data from miscue analysis and determine the instructional support an individual student needs. Debra Goodman offers two additional forms for collecting and analyzing miscue data: **Reader-Selected Miscues** and **Profile of Reading Strategy Use**.

WHAT ELSE?

The most important use of miscue analysis is to help teachers and researchers gain insight into the reading process. Secondly, as teachers analyze the extent to which a student's miscues change, disrupt, or enhance the meaning of a written text, they acquire specific information about the student's reading ability. Teachers can then plan sensitive instruction and curriculum that build on the student's strengths rather than weaknesses. Finally, miscue analysis also helps teachers evaluate reading material, determining whether a given selection should be used in a reading program and how suitable it is for an individual student.

References

Goodman, Y., and Burke, C. 1980. *Reading strategies: Focus on comprehension.* Katonah, NY: Richard C. Owen.

Goodman, K., Goodman, Y., and Bird, L. B. 1992. *Whole language catalog: Supplement on authentic assessment.* Santa Rosa, CA: American School Publishers.

Goodman, Y., Watson, D., and Burke, C. 1987. *Reading miscue inventory: Alternative procedures.* Katonah, NY: Richard C. Owen.

See: OBSERVING p. 69; ANALYZING pp. 157, 160, 163

General Procedure for Marking Miscues, Miscue Analysis Procedure III Questions, and Miscue Analysis Procedure IV Individual Conference Form were developed by Yetta M. Goodman, Carolyn Burke, and Dorothy Watson.

Reader-Selected Miscues and Profile of Reading Strategy Use were developed by Debra Goodman.

General Procedure for Marking Miscues

Substitutions
Write the miscue above the appropriate text:
There
Where is Sven?

this is a
"No," said the voice.

Was something wrong with Papa?

Omissions
Circle the omitted text item: We thought (up) different ways to jump.

Insertions
Write the OR above the caret ∧ used to mark the insertion: First listen ∧

is
The other way ∧ to take care of your heart.

Repetitions
Draw a line under the repeated text portion and up in front of the first word, ending in a circle. The letter in the circle shows the reason for regressing.

1. Anticipating and reflecting: Ⓡ The village where I grew up …

2. Repeating and correcting: Ⓒ *feels* Ⓒ *c—* Ⓒ *oranges*
   Blood feeds all the cells and organs.

3. Repeating and abandoning a correct form: Ⓐ̶Ⓒ *complaining*
   She was always comparing.

4. Repeating and unsuccessfully attempting to correct: *Clarida* *Clarence*
   Her name was Claribie.

5. Repeating that affects more than one miscue: Ⓒ *sense* Ⓥ̶Ⓒ
   … the heart is a sensitive machine …

Additional Markings
1. Partials: Ⓒ *por—*
   The man left the porridge …

2. Nonword substitutions: $distroubles
   If it bothers you to think of it as baby sitting …

3. Dialect misarticulations and other language variations: *likes*
   … just about everybody likes babies.
   $pecific
   He had a specific place in mind.
   hangabers
   They make hamburgers over the fire.

4. Intonation shifts: *récord*
   He will record her voice.

5. Split syllables: The li|ttle girl yelled her head off.

6. Pauses: *2 sec.*
   … do all day| while I am away cutting wood?"

Miscue Analysis Procedure III Questions

Question 1: Syntactic Acceptability
Is the sentence syntactically acceptable in the reader's dialect and within the context of the entire selection?

> Y—The sentence, as finally produced by the reader, is syntactically acceptable.
>
> N—The sentence, as finally produced by the reader, is not syntactically acceptable (partial acceptability is not considered in this procedure).

Question 2: Semantic Acceptability
Is the sentence semantically acceptable in the reader's dialect and within the context of the entire selection? (Question 2 cannot be coded Y if Question 1 has been coded N.)

> Y—The sentence, as finally produced by the reader, is semantically acceptable.
>
> N—The sentence, as finally produced by the reader, is not semantically acceptable (partial acceptability is not considered in this procedure).

Question 3: Meaning Change
Does the sentence, as finally produced by the reader, change the meaning of the selection? (Question 3 is coded only if Questions 1 and 2 are coded.)

> N—There is no change in the meaning of the selection.
>
> P—There is inconsistency, loss, or change of a minor idea, incident, character, fact sequence, or concept in the selection.
>
> Y—There is inconsistency, loss, or change of a major idea, incident, character, fact sequence, or concept in the selection.

Question 4: Graphic Similarity
How much does the miscue look like the text item?

> H—A high degree of graphic similarity exists between the miscue and the text.
>
> S—Some degree of graphic similarity exists between the miscue and the text.
>
> N—No degree of graphic similarity exists between the miscue and the text.

Miscue Analysis Procedure IV Individual Conference Form

Reader _____ Date _____ Grade/Age _____

Teacher _____

Selection _____

Mark all sentences in a complete story or article using the following question:
Does the sentence, as the reader left it, make sense within the context of the story?

Yes _____ Total _____

No _____ Total _____

Number of Sentences _____ Comprehending Score _____

Divide total Yes by total Number of Sentences for Comprehending Score
_____

Retelling Information

Comments

Reader-Selected Miscues

Name _____ Name of Story _____ Date _____

Page No.	What did the reader say?	What did the book say?	Did the miscue make sense? Yes	No	If no, was reader using story language? using letter sounds?	Did the miscue change the story meaning? Yes	No	Is this a good miscue?

Comments:

Profile of Reading Strategy Use

Name _____ Date _____ Grade _____

	Semantic	Syntactic	Graphophonic
P R E D I C T I N G			
	Corrections		
C O N F I R M I N G			
I N T E G R A T I N G		**Objectives** 1. _____ _____ 2. _____ _____ 3. _____ _____ 4. _____ _____ 5. _____ _____	

Miscue Analysis Form

WHO?

All readers.

WHY?

Connie Weaver explains: "As you analyze the miscues, keep in mind that you bring your own schemas to your reading of the text as well as to your analysis and evaluation of the reader's miscues. The meaning of a text is created by each reader uniquely. If this seems appallingly subjective, remember that machine-scored standardized tests only appear to provide an objective measure of students' reading ability. As a test-taker, I'd rather have a human being trying to understand my subjective responses than a computer providing a numerical score without any ability to analyze or understand what good reasons I might have had for doing what I did."

HOW?

Before analyzing and coding the miscues, it helps to read the completed worksheet once or twice, reproducing all the miscues made by the reader. This should give you a better feel for the reader's strategies. Then you will be ready to transfer the miscue data to the **Miscue Analysis Form**.

For each miscue numbered for analysis, you will first need to indicate what the text said and what the reader said. This information should be entered in the "Text" and "Reader" columns, respectively. Then, for each miscue you can ask the following five questions. Keep in mind that if the miscue is grammatically and semantically appropriate for the reader's dialect, it should be coded as entirely acceptable (checked under Yes in columns 1, 2, 3, and 5).

0. *WAS THE MISCUE DIALECT-RELATED OR RELATED TO THE READER'S SPEAKING ENGLISH AS A SECOND OR SUBSEQUENT LANGUAGE?* If a miscue simply reflects a different sound system in the reader's dialect or native language, it is ordinarily not listed on the coding sheet at all. But if it reflects a grammatical pattern common in the reader's dialect or reflects imperfect mastery of the grammar of English because the person does not speak English natively, then the miscue is noted on the coding form *but coded as completely acceptable in columns 1, 2, 3, and 5*. If there are many such miscues in the reading sample, then more than twenty-five miscues will need to be coded in order to provide insights into the reader's strategies. Some of the most common of the ESL-related grammatical miscues are the omission of inflectional endings ("he go" for *he goes*, "he walk" for *he walked*) the use of an inflectional ending in a verb where none is needed ("he wanted to goed"), the inappropriate omission or use of articles (*a*, *an*, and *the*), or inappropriate use of one preposition for another ("at" for *in*, for example).

1. *DID THE MISCUE GO WITH THE PRECEDING CONTEXT?* If the answer is a simple yes, put a check in the Yes column. *Consider the miscue acceptable with preceding context if it resulted in a meaningful sequence of words, up to and including the miscue—even if the meaning is clearly changed.* Questions 3a and 3b require looking at whether or not the miscue significantly changes or affects the meaning of the sentence or the selection, but Questions 1 and 2 are designed to give credit for meaningful sentences, even if that meaning appears not to be "the same" meaning. If the

miscue fits with the preceding grammar but not with the preceding meaning (or vice versa), put a check in the column labeled Partially; then add a G to indicate that it fits with the grammar, or an M to indicate that it fits with meaning. If the miscue was not at all acceptable with preceding context, put a check in the No column. In trying to decide whether the miscue fits with the preceding context, read the preceding part of the sentence the way it finally ended up, perhaps with some miscues uncorrected but others corrected.

2. *DID THE MISCUE GO WITH THE FOLLOWING CONTEXT?* Follow essentially the same procedure as explained in Question 1, but this time examine only the miscue and what immediately follows it in the sentence.

3a. *WAS THE ESSENTIAL MEANING OF THE SENTENCE LEFT INTACT?* This is clearly the most subjective of the questions. Some teachers steeped in the notion that good reading must be word-perfect reading want to code *any* departure from the text as changing essential meaning. However, this is contrary to the whole purpose and spirit of miscue analysis. If only part of the essential meaning seems to be lost, or if it seems impossible to decide, one can put a check on the line between Yes and No. Otherwise, check either Yes or No. This column helps us draw inferences about the reader's ability to construct meaning at the sentence level, with the particular text in question.

3b. *WAS THE ESSENTIAL MEANING OF THE STORY LEFT INTACT?* Particularly with stories, it is rare that a single miscue disrupts the essential meaning of the entire reading selection. If it clearly does, check No, indicating that the meaning was not left intact, or put a check on the line, indicating indeterminacy or uncertainty. Otherwise, check Yes. Most people find that all or almost all of the reader's miscues receive a Yes in this column. Why bother including it, then? Because teachers just coming to understand miscues and miscue analysis can learn a lot about reading itself by considering how unimportant each individual miscue often is, at the story or whole-text level. Concomitantly, the results in column 3b may give teachers a greater appreciation for some readers' ability to grasp the essential meaning of a text despite numerous miscues that seem not to preserve the meaning of individual sentences.

4. *WAS THE MISCUE CORRECTED?* If so, put a check in the Yes column. If not, put a check under No. If unsuccessful attempts at correction were marked on the coding sheet, one might want to put a check on the borderline between the two columns, indicating that the reader at least attempted to correct.

5. *WAS THE MISCUE EITHER MEANING-PRESERVING OR CORRECTED?* The point here is that if the miscue preserved essential meaning at the sentence level (column 3a), there was no need for the miscue to be corrected. On the other hand, if the miscue didn't preserve meaning but was corrected (column 4), that too means that ultimately the miscue reflected no essential loss of meaning. In other words, check Yes in column 5 if the miscue received a Yes in either column 3a or 4; otherwise, check the No column. (If some miscues were marked as partially acceptable in column 3a, they can again be checked on the borderline between Yes and No in column 5, unless they were corrected; in that case, they automatically receive a Yes in column 5.) In effect, the Yes column here indicates which miscues initially or ultimately resulted in *no significant loss of comprehension* at the sentence level.

— Adapted from *Reading Process and Practice: From Socio-Psycholinguistics to Whole Language* (2nd ed. Portsmouth, NH: Heinemann, 1994).

See: OBSERVING p. 69; ANALYZING pp. 151, 160, 163

Miscue Analysis Form was developed by Connie Weaver, professor of English at Western Michigan University, Kalamazoo.

Miscue Analysis Form

Reader's name _____

Date _____

Reading selection: _____

TEXT	READER	Was the miscue dialect-related or ESL-related? 0		Did the miscue go with the preceding context? 1			Did the miscue go with the following context? 2			Was the essential meaning of the **sentence** left intact? 3A		Was the essential meaning of the **story** left intact? 3B		Was the miscue corrected? 4		Was the miscue either meaning preserving or corrected? 5 (cols. 3A & 4)	
		Yes	No	Yes	Partially	No	Yes	Partially	No	Yes	No	Yes	No	Yes	No	Yes	No
1																	
2																	
3																	
4																	
5																	
6																	
7																	
8																	
9																	
10																	
11																	
12																	
13																	
14																	
15																	
16																	
17																	
18																	
19																	
20																	
21																	
22																	
23																	
24																	
25																	
TOTALS																	
PERCENTS																	

Miscue Analysis: Retelling Summary

WHO? _____

All readers.

WHY? _____

Retelling has always been an integral part of miscue analysis because making sense through a transaction with the written text is ongoing and cumulative. An understanding of the reader's comprehension after the reading can be inferred from the retelling. Retellings can be evaluated statistically and used as a measure of comprehension. It is important to consider that the measure is only a glimpse of what any reader knows. Readers seldom provide complete retellings. A retelling score only measures what the reader chooses to share about the reading.

HOW? _____

All presentations can be done singly or in groups. Each presentation provides a legitimate opportunity to evaluate the reader's comprehension. Retellings require practice by both teacher and reader. Since it is important for readers to discover their own personal responses, teachers need to avoid giving signals about the appropriateness of the retelling. Readers' retelling scores usually increase over time, because the teacher gets better at conducting the retelling and the students improve as they become more comfortable with the procedures.

Some teachers eventually have their students read a story for miscue analysis purposes into a tape recorder and follow up with an unaided retelling without the teacher present. This is especially helpful for those teachers who want the evaluative information that miscue analysis provides for all students, but who don't have the time to sit down with each student two or three times a year. The student records both the reading and the retelling, and the teacher analyzes the tape later at a more convenient time. This, of course, would only be done with students who have become very familiar with miscue procedures. For a more authentic response, some teachers have the reader retell to another student in the class who has not read the material.

There are three parts to a retelling: unaided, aided, and specific. The unaided retelling is always done immediately following the reading. The other kinds of retellings take place depending on the teacher's purposes.

THE UNAIDED RETELLING. The unaided part of the retelling allows the reader to tell whatever they remember. It is usually cued when the teacher asks, "Remember, I told you I'd ask you about the story when you finished? Would you please tell me what you remember?" During the unaided retelling, the teacher does not interrupt or cue the student in any way, although the teacher should show an interest in the retelling. When the reader seems to be finished, the teacher might want to wait for thirty to forty-five seconds. Waiting time seems to spur some readers to expand on their unaided retelling. Broad questions such as "Anything more?" or "What else do you remember?" may be used to encourage more unaided retelling at the very end.

THE AIDED RETELLING. Aided retelling is used to encourage students to expand on their unaided retelling. Teachers' questions and the way they respond to the answers are of great importance. The teacher must avoid giving students information about a story or article by asking very specific questions. Using the student's own language from the retelling, such as names for people and concepts, the teacher asks open-ended questions: "You said it was a $typsical [meaning typical] baby, tell me more about what that means."

THE SPECIFIC RETELLING. This is an in-depth retelling used by some teachers which can help evaluate the reader's comprehension and move very specifically into an instructional strategy. Asking a reader to point out places in the text that seemed confusing, or to tell the teacher about words or ideas that were unclear provide additional evaluative information as well as provide the opportunity for an instructional strategy immediately following the reading experience.

WHAT ELSE?

Retellings can take many forms. They can be oral or written. In addition to retellings, teachers can evaluate readers' comprehension through a variety of presentations. There are many ways to graphically represent a story. Readers can sketch, diagram, map, draw, or create timelines or story game boards. And, of course, there is a wide range of dramatic forms in which readers can engage. Nonfiction reading lends itself to different presentations such as report writing, debates, and speeches. Anecdotal records or audiotapes of the presentations can be kept for evaluation over time.

Reference

Goodman, Y., Watson, D., and Burke, C. 1987. *Reading miscue inventory: Alternative procedures.* Katonah, NY: Richard C. Owen.

See: OBSERVING p. 69; ANALYZING pp. 151, 157, 163

Miscue Analysis: Retelling Summary was developed by Yetta M. Goodman, professor of Reading, Language, and Culture at the University of Arizona, Tucson.

Miscue Analysis: Retelling Summary

Name ——————————————————————— Date ———————— Grade ———

Selection ——

Holistic Retelling Score (optional)

Plot Statements:

Theme Statements:

Inferences:

Misconceptions:

Comments:

Retrospective and Collaborative Miscue Analysis

WHO?

Retrospective miscue analysis (RMA) and collaborative retrospective miscue analysis (CRMA) has been used with adults, high school students, middle school students, and, conceptually, with elementary students. All related research shows that students gain in self-confidence and self-assurance.

WHY?

RMA and CRMA are authentic assessments that help teachers understand what students know and do in the process of reading. RMA and CRMA also invite students to engage in self-reflection and qualitatively assess their miscues and the strategies they incorporate when reading.

HOW?

RMA and CRMA can be conducted in a variety of groupings: teacher/student, teacher/small group, teacher/class, and collaborative peer groups. The procedure follows the same format outlined in *Reading Miscue Inventory* (Goodman, Burke, and Watson, 1987). Readers are asked to read a complete text into a tape recorder. They are informed that they will be asked to give a retelling of the story at the end of the reading. The teacher completes the analysis to identify readers' strengths and weaknesses. The teacher also interviews the readers using the **Retrospective and Collaborative Miscue Analysis** form, helping them to define their beliefs and perceptions about the reading process and discussing the strategies they are utilizing. As professional educators, teachers must decide which miscues and strategies to select and discuss with their students. They base their decisions on the needs of their students, their students' confidence in themselves as readers, and the strategies they are using efficiently and inefficiently. Usually six to ten miscues are discussed. Initially, it is best to focus only on readers' strengths until they become comfortable with the procedure.

In a CRMA, students are not forced to read aloud in the group; however, it is the role of the facilitator to create an environment in which, eventually, all students will feel comfortable doing so. Students are grouped heterogeneously; therefore, a variety of texts are necessary to meet their needs. The collaborative grouping helps the classroom teacher, who can rarely work with just one student for long periods of time. The teacher may tape the discussion or take notes during the session recording students' strengths, weaknesses, and use of strategies.

Students can also work in heterogeneous groups without a teacher. Initially, they explore ideas about miscues with the teacher in a whole-class setting or in small groups. Students are taught about miscues and the reading process during mini-lessons, miscues are discussed when the teacher reads with the students individually; and, the teacher discusses efficient and inefficient strategies when students read in the group setting. Students should understand that all readers make miscues and that some strategies are more effective than others in creating meaning while reading. The goal is not to test the reader but to have students discuss reading in a meaningful way in the context of real reading.

One student is taped reading aloud. The students listen to the tape, stopping it when they hear a miscue. They then discuss the miscue and suggest reasons for it. The miscue session can be audiotaped or videotaped, or students can take notes on the discussion. Near the end of the session, the teacher joins the groups to discuss any problems, questions, or strategies the students may have about the session.

WHAT ELSE?

When students have the opportunity to observe other readers as well as themselves engaged in the reading process, they learn that many of the strategies they use are effective and efficient, facilitating understanding, while others are inefficient, disrupting meaning. While observing the reading process, they begin to view errors qualitatively rather than quantitatively. Sampling, predicting, and confirming all support readers in their quest for meaning, while reading every word, finger pointing, and sounding out words adversely affect reading comprehension. With this awareness, students can alter their reading strategies accordingly.

References

Goodman, Y., Watson, D., and Burke, C. 1987. *Reading miscue inventory: Alternative procedures*. Katonah, NY: Richard C. Owen.

Goodman, Y., and Marek, A. 1989, October. *Retrospective miscue analysis analysis*. Occasional Papers. Program in Language and Literacy, College of Education , University of Arizona, Tucson.

See: OBSERVING p. 69; ANALYZING pp. 151, 157

Retrospective and Collaborative Miscue Analysis was developed by Yetta M. Goodman and Ann Marek and is used in the classroom by Sarah Costello, a language arts teacher at Pistor Middle School in Tucson, AZ.

Retrospective and Collaborative Miscue Analysis

1. Does the miscue make sense?

2. In what way does it make sense? In what way doesn't it make sense?

3. Did you correct yourself when you made your miscue?

4. Why do you think you made this miscue?

5. Think of as many possible reasons for this miscue as you can.

Editing Checklist ·
Peer Editing Checklist

WHO?

These guidelines serve elementary students, kindergarten through secondary, with some adjustment for young, developing writers.

WHY?

Many teachers who invite their students to write daily about topics of their own choosing have found it helpful to create forms that help students monitor their writing experiences.

HOW?

Editing Checklist and **Peer Editing Checklist** guide students through the editing process. Once students have reached what they consider their final draft, they self-edit using a form such as the ones shown here. Teachers can develop a whole-class editing checklist and display it on a chart in the room for all to see, or students can keep photocopies of the checklist in their writing folders. Some teachers prefer to create an individual checklist for each student that is tailored to fit each individual's developing editing skills.

Many teachers ask their students to edit using a colored pencil. The teacher uses a different colored pencil for additional editing. In this way, there is a record of the editing done by both the student and teacher on each final draft.

WHAT ELSE?

It is helpful to introduce kindergarten students to the full writing process using the professional writing vocabulary such as drafting, revision, and editing. Even though kindergartners cannot edit for the full range of conventions represented on these forms, they can use a form tailor-made for developing writers and check for such things as whether they've written their name on their piece, included the date and page numbers, included any accompanying illustrations, and so forth.

Some teachers invite their students to serve as peer editors for each other. Peer editors read and re-read the author's piece, completing a peer-editing form as they carefully consider each editorial concern.

See: INTERACTING p. 123

Editing Checklist was developed by Avery D. Walker, first/second-grade teacher at Ohlone School in Palo Alto, CA.

Peer Editing Checklist was developed by teachers Dan Adcock, Carole Addis, Anne Hackley, Gerrie Jeske, Catherine Schuck, and Lori Shaw at Lowell Elementary School, Missoula, MT.

Editing Checklist

Name _____ Date _____ Grade _____

Edited by _____

Story Name _____ Author _____

Capitalization

_____ Sentences start with a capital

_____ Names begin with a capital

_____ Each word in title begins with a capital

Punctuation

_____ Each sentence ends with a period or other appropriate ending punctuation

_____ Quotation marks are used when someone talks

_____ Commas are used

General

_____ Most words are spelled correctly

_____ The story makes sense

_____ Neat handwriting

Editing Marks

¶ new paragraph

◯ misspelled word

∧ add word or punctuation

take out a word

move a word

≡ capitalize

Peer Editing Checklist

Name _____ Date _____ Grade _____

Story Content

1. What did you enjoy about the story?

2. Does it make sense to you?

3. What ideas do you have that would make the story clearer or more interesting?

Story Form

1. Does each sentence start with a capital letter?

2. Are capital letters used with names of people, countries, nationalities, days of the week, names of months, holidays, and titles?

3. Is there a punctuation mark at the end of every sentence: a period (.), a question mark (?), or an exclamation point (!)?

4. Are there quotation marks ("") whenever people are talking?

5. Are commas used when there is a list of things or when a pause is needed?

6. Is each word spelled right?

7. What will the author do next?

_____   _____
Signature of author   Signature of editor

Qualities of Effective Writing · Outstanding Poetic Qualities

WHO? _____

With some adaptation for primary students, these forms will work for all students and teachers.

WHY? _____

What is good writing? It's a question that must be asked and answered before one can get down to the business of evaluating writing. The answer will evolve throughout the year as teachers and children experiment with their own writing and continuously refine their understanding of writing and how it is best developed. And it will evolve as teachers and children share and discuss models of good writing found in published fiction, nonfiction, poetry, and plays by professional authors.

HOW? _____

Teachers who are striving to nurture competent, creative writers will routinely draw from three primary sources to help their students develop a sense of good writing:

PUBLISHED WRITING. Frank Smith reminds us that we learn best through "demonstrations," by watching someone as an apprentice watches a craftsperson engaged in doing that which we desire to learn. Just as every act provides a demonstration, so every artifact teaches something. Thus, every time we open up the pages of a novel, we encounter a wide range of demonstrations regarding many aspects of fiction writing. At a global level, we receive lessons in sense of story, theme, and character development, while at the same time we learn the particulars of writing conventions: paragraphing, spelling, punctuation, and so forth.

Teachers may build on the lessons printed material provides by reading aloud a wide range of genre, and then highlighting through talk one or two aspects (Edelsky, 1986). For example, those teachers who want to help their students understand the techniques authors use to create full-bodied characters might point to the unique strategy that Patricia MacLachlan uses to introduce the reader to Sarah in her Newberry Award winner, *Sarah, Plain and Tall*. At the beginning of the book, the lead characters exchange a series of letters, giving the reader important insights into Sarah before she has even arrived on the scene. Teachers can help their students understand and appreciate this technique by talking about it after the read-aloud.

CHILDREN'S WRITING. In effective writing classrooms, there is as much talk about writing as there is actual writing, and teachers pursue every opportunity to showcase a particular technique or writing convention that students have tried or used especially well. For instance, during an all-group-share, fourth-grade teacher Ray Dawley noted that Maricela had opened her story with dialogue; he then engaged his students in a discussion regarding different leads. His celebration of Maricela's lead, together with the discussion about different tactics authors employ to open a piece, helped the students understand the importance of a good lead, and inspired many to experiment later with alternative approaches in their own writing.

TEACHER'S WRITING. Graves (1989) remarked once that among the talented writing teachers he and his colleague Jane Hanson were working with in New Hampshire, one in particular stood out because of the quality and quantity of student writing that came out of her classroom. The one variable between her classroom and the others seemed to be that she routinely set aside fifteen minutes every day to write with her students and also made a point of openly discussing her writing with them. By demonstrating through their own writing the range of decisions writers must wrestle with as they create meaning through print, teachers may provide particularly powerful lessons about what constitutes effective writing: why one verb is stronger than another, why one snippet of dialogue works well, why one piece resonates with voice, and so forth.

WHAT ELSE?

Although discerning good writing clearly takes time, in order to help with the evolutionary process, we've included two lists for teachers to consider. **Qualities of Effective Writing** draws from the work of such writing experts as Nancie Atwell, Lucy Calkins, Donald Graves, and Donald Murray. Note that it not only includes the qualities and mechanics of an effective writing product, but also asks the evaluator to consider the process the author used in creating the composition. **Outstanding Poetic Qualities** is from Jack Collom, a poet who works with the Teachers and Writers Collaborative in New York City. In his book, *Moving Windows: Evaluating the Poetry Children Write* (1985), Collom lists the outstanding poetic qualities he painstakingly culled from his extensive collection of children's poetry.

References

Atwell, N. 1987. *In the middle: Writing, reading and learning.* Portsmouth, NH: Heinemann.

Calkins, L. 1986. *The art of teaching.* Portsmouth, NH: Heinemann.

Collom, J. 1985. *Moving windows: Evaluating the poetry children write.* New York: Teachers and Writers Collaborative.

Edelsky, C. 1986. *Literature studies.* Redwood City, CA: Redwood City School District Inservice.

Graves, D. 1983. *Writing: Teachers and children at work.* Portsmouth, NH: Heinemann.

See: OBSERVING pp. 74, 81

Qualities of Effective Writing was developed by Lois Bridges Bird.

Outstanding Poetic Qualities was developed by Jack Collom, a poet with the Teachers and Writers Collaborative in New York City.

Qualities of Effective Writing

Name _____ Date _____ Grade _____

Quality of Expression:
_____ inclusion of detail
_____ voice
_____ sense of story, logical sequence
_____ strong verbs and nouns
_____ strong lead, strong ending
_____ focus
_____ unity and clarity
_____ coherence
_____ character development
_____ effective dialogue
_____ literary techniques
_____ complex sentences

Process of Writing:
_____ topic selection
_____ revision strategies/ability to revise
_____ ability to share writing
_____ use of pictures to help carry the meaning
_____ ability to label a picture or write a narrative
_____ purpose for writing
_____ risk-taking
_____ proofreading
_____ experiments with different styles

Mechanics:
_____ spelling
_____ punctuation
_____ handwriting
_____ paragraph breaks
_____ spaces
_____ upper/lower case
_____ left-to-right directionality
_____ grammar
_____ capitalization

Outstanding Poetic Qualities

_____ CANDIDNESS AND INNOCENCE:

This refers to the simple, unfettered realism children can have; the ability to see a thing as it is, not as it may fit one's world view. Children certainly have biases, but these tend to be transparent. Kids are also more capable of obvious contradiction, which helps in poetry, as Whitman let us know. These qualities lead not only to pure, simple "takes" on what's seen but also to revelations of the human mind and to original use of language.

_____ ENERGY:

Kids can often leap about rapidly in a richness of ideas and get this into their poems. Their verbal energy, once it's rolling, tends to be uninhibited. They also frequently invest their surroundings with a sense of life, speaking of even inanimate objects as if they had their own wills and spirits.

_____ SURPRISE:

Partly because their thoughts are not routinized, kids are likely to respond to the newness of each detail, which allows the natural surprises of the world to turn up in their writings. Their attention dances about, frustrating to teacher or parent but a possible source of creative power. They also like to surprise, perhaps as a way of being themselves in the face of all they're learning. They create incongruities for the fun of it.

_____ SOUND:

Rhythm and all the music of talk and poetry, including rhyme, assonance, and alliteration as well as poems showing repetition, extended lists, and onomatopoeia. A physical cluster of qualities is involved here; there's little barrier between kids and music. Children's great fault, in regard to soundplay, lies in its uncritical use, but they often demonstrate a delicate feel for music in words, especially when the writing is unstructured. Though children need direction, they usually lack the wide command of detail to work well in a highly restrictive form, such as set rhyme scheme. Their sense of rhythm emerges best when based on their own speech patterns.

_____ MOVES:

This means surprise as a recurrent quality of the language—sophisticated surprise that seems to emphasize the shifts in meaning more than the shock itself.

_____ SHOW-DON'T-TELL:

Keeping the attention on the sensory, not the abstract.

_____ SURREALISM AND METAPHOR:

Images from the mind. Surrealism uses connections from dreams and unconscious (or connections resembling those); metaphor connects, via one's thought, one object to another, usually in the external world.

_____ CONCISION, SHAPELINESS, AND UNDERSTANDING:

Shortening, shaping, and shutting up.

_____ EMPATHY:

According to its roots, empathy means "feel in" (whereas sympathy means "feel with"). The quality of reaching outside the self and becoming affected by the circumstances there.

Looking Closer at a Writing Sample

WHO?

Upper-elementary through middle school students.

WHY?

Debra Goodman is required to grade her students in English and spelling, and she uses their writing samples to help her evaluate her students' development as writers as well as to assign grades.

HOW?

Debra explains: "I use a writing sample from students' regular classwork, rather than ask them to write solely for the purpose of evaluation. I prefer a writing piece that will be 'published' in some way, so that I can look at the student's revision and editing strategies. I follow a simple yet thorough process:

1. I start with a revision conference with the student, looking closely at the style and quality of the writing. In such conferences, I have learned to focus on the story or report as a whole and not on specific wordings or spellings. With this focus, students will often revise by rewriting entire sections of the text, and particular wordings or spellings become unimportant for the time being.

2. I make a copy of the rough draft in order to look at it more carefully. If there are confusing passages or grammatical passages in the story, I try to determine why the writer 'miscued.' Sometimes a piece that seems very confusing turns out to have only one or two problems. I almost always improve my view of a student's ability by taking the time to study a piece of writing.

3. **Looking Closer at a Writing Sample** enables me to discover the writer's strengths. I keep this form in a looseleaf binder that I use as my gradebook. It contains a divider for each child, with a sheet for reflecting on his or her writing. I place the rough draft in my gradebook so that it can be compared with previous samples. I focus my comments on the writer's capabilities and strengths.

4. After I look at the quality and style of a piece of writing, I ask the student to count the words in the first (and second) drafts. While longer is not always better, the number of words that a student writes indicates his or her interest in writing. If a child consistently writes very short pieces, it might indicate that he or she needs some strategies for adding details and descriptions to the writing.

5. I ask students to circle the words they feel are spelled wrong in their rough draft. Then I read through the rough draft and check all the spellings. I figure out the percentage of words spelled correctly, and I sometimes write this score directly on the report card under 'Spelling.' Or, I determine a letter grade based on the student's percentage, improvement, or proofreading skills.

WHAT ELSE?

"I also keep a quantitative checklist of the student's writing. I count the number of journal entries, pieces and pages in the writing folder, letters that a student writes, etc. These numbers assist me in giving the student the required letter grade in English and to justify this grade to parents and colleagues."

See: OBSERVING p. 74

Looking Closer at a Writing Sample was developed by Debra Goodman, who teaches fifth grade at the Dewey Learning Center in Detroit, MI.

Looking Closer at a Writing Sample

Name _____ Date _____ Grade _____

1. Is the writing clear and meaningful?

2. Is it organized in an appropriate format?

3. Is the writer able to present information, express a viewpoint, or tell a story?

4. Is the piece interesting to read?

5. Is the writer communicating with an audience in mind?

6. Is there evidence of the writer's voice?

7. Is there evidence of the writer's understanding of plot, characterization, or other literary techniques?

8. Are there some signs of beauty or brilliance?

Reporting: Summing Up

Learning Logs

WHO?

All students, with some adaptation for primary students.

WHY?

As writing breaks down the artificial walls separating one subject from another, it also provides a path to understanding for the learner and, equally important, for the teacher eager to follow the student's journey of discovery.

HOW?

Debra Goodman explains how she uses **Learning Logs** in her fifth-grade class: "Rather than develop a quiz of what I would like my students to know, I simply ask, 'What have you learned?' Their responses vary widely, as I invite them to tell me what they feel is significant about their learning experiences. Students do better in this alternative to quizzes or tests because they all have something to share. Each Friday we take out our learning journals and write down what we learned that week. As we are getting started, I ask who would like to share something they have learned. We continue to discuss the topic until we have explored the specific details involved. Through these weekly discussions, the students learn to give examples and details of their learning. Instead of general comments such as 'I learned about math,' they explain, 'I learned a new math game with fraction bars that helped me understand how fractions work.'"

WHAT ELSE?

Rena Malkofsky, a third/fourth-grade teacher at El Carmelo School in Palo Alto, California, is an enthusiastic user of learning logs. Her students keep logs for math, science, and reading in addition to writing notebooks and portfolios. Rena says that she wouldn't know how to teach without learning logs, because they enable her to follow her students' line of thinking, identify possible holes in their logic, and respond directly to their instructional needs. Students benefit as well. The logs enable them to control their own learning, to have a clear sense of what and how they are learning, and to evaluate their own progress. For example, Rena requires that her students complete a weekly math puzzle that entails four steps:

1. Write the problem in the student's own words.
2. Solve the problem.
3. Explain in the student's math log how he or she solved it.
4. Share their method with a friend.

The end result is that the kids now really understand that they have to explain their thinking—getting the right answer is not enough—they have to understand *how* they got it.

See: REPORTING p. 193

Learning Log

(sample notebook page)

ERICA   4/2/92

Math   puzzle

Make a dollar out of thirteen coins.

MY ANSWER How I did it →

It was challenging, but it was worth it,
and I had a "lot" of fun!!! Well, I got a
peice of paper and a pencil. I made four
circles at the left edge in a line going down
Then I wrote the numbers 25 in one circle 10 in
one circle, five in one circle, and one in the last
circle. Then I made about four circles after
each one. (Example: 〇〇〇〇〇) Then I put a dot
in a circle in the 〇〇〇〇〇 25th section, then I put
a dot in the ten th 〇〇〇〇〇 section. And I kept on
picking numbers 〇〇〇〇〇 and making dots
and then I counted it up and... bingo! I had
my answer.
        I shared it with...
        I shared this math puzzle with
my mom.

Literature Studies Guidelines · Literature Response Guide · Literature Circles

WHO?

Jann Ching developed Literature Response Guide for use with her sixth-grade students whom she felt needed support in discussing literature. Greg Chapnick asks all his sixth-grade students to follow his Literature Studies Guidelines. With some adaptation, both guides will work well with both older and younger students.

WHY?

Students who participate in literature studies are often responsible for reading a book on their own, responding to and reflecting on the reading in a literature log, and coming to their study group prepared to discuss their book. Afterwards, they may revisit the text, rereading with a more analytical focus. A guide such as **Literature Studies Guidelines** helps them keep track of the study process.

Students develop an appreciation for literature when they are given the time to respond to the reading with other students. Generally, literature-circle discussions are open ended. Students respond freely in their discussions; however, for students who need support the **Literature Response Guide** provides a helpful structure.

HOW?

Greg Chapnick reviews literature studies and the guidelines with his students several times, working through the guidelines first as a whole class. Each student receives the guidelines and refers to them as needed. In Jann Ching's class, after all students in each literature circle complete their literature logs using her guideline sheet, they take turns sharing their summaries, reactions, and excerpts. In this way, they learn to respond to each others' reactions and improve the quality of group discussions.

WHAT ELSE?

The **Literature Circles** sheet is used to record each student's understanding of his or her reading. This sheet enables Jann to keep more accurate records on her students' progress, to monitor their pace, and to keep track of the book that each group of students is working on. The comments section enables her to record authentic observations and evaluations of each child's reading progress. At the end of each evaluation period, she refers to the data on this form to summarize each student's reading progress.

See: MONITORING pp. 14, 20; INTERACTING p. 118

Literature Response Guide and Literature Circles were developed by Jann Pataray Ching, a sixth-grade teacher at Benjamin Parker School in Kaneohe, HI, and a graduate student at Indiana University.

Literature Studies Guidelines was developed by Greg Chapnick, a sixth-grade teacher at Lorin Eden School in Hayward, CA.

Literature Studies Guidelines

1. You must read your assigned book at least once by the deadline agreed upon by the group and the teacher. If you finish your book early, you should re-read the book or find another to read. You must be ready and prepared to discuss your book at the first group meeting. Use post-its to mark sections of the book that are special or that confuse you.

2. Write in your literature log at least two times weekly. You can use the checklist in the front of your log to check off these times. You should be writing about your thoughts about your book, not just telling what happened. Guide questions for literature log comments are:
   a. What parts made you think?
   b. What did you think?
   c. Does it remind you of anything?
   d. Make predictions.
   e. Ask questions (and answer them).
   f. Other ideas or comments.

3. Come to your group meeting on time. Bring paper, pencil, your book, and your literature log (if needed).

4. You make the group work. Do not join us unless you are prepared to listen to each other, respond to each other, and share your thoughts about literature. You are graded on finishing the book on time, participating in the group discussion (talking at the right time, listening at all other times), and completing and sharing your assignment.

5. When you get an assignment, it should be done as follows:
   a. Put your name, date, and number on top of page.
   b. Write the title of the book as the main heading.
   c. Listen and write down the assignments as given.
   d. If there is more than one part to the assignment, make sure you put a short heading above each section so that we know what your sections are about.

Literature Response Guide

Name _____

DIRECTIONS: Complete this worksheet in your literature logs (do not write on this form). Give and receive feedback on your summary, reactions, and your chosen sentences (Part III) by discussing each in your literature circle.

Story/Book Title: _____

Page numbers/chapters that you read: _____

I. SUMMARY: In your own words, include the following:

- characters

- main character's problem

- main events that led to solving the problem

- climax

- resolution

II. REACTIONS: React to the reading and explain your answers (choose any 3).

1. How did a character feel when faced with a certain situation? (interpret)

2. Why did the character react the way he/she did? (interpret)

3. Should the character have reacted the way he/she did? (judge)

4. What would you do if you were one of the characters? (analyze/synthesize)

5. How should have the character reacted in the situation? (evaluate)

6. How does the story relate to your experiences? (synthesize)

7. What do the events in the story remind you of? (synthesize)

8. Why do you like/dislike the reading so far? Explain. (evaluate/analyze)

9. What do you think will happen next? (predict)

10. If you were the writer of this story, what events would you include in this story. What will happen to the character? How would you end this story? (analyze/synthesize)

III. IMPROVING YOUR WRITING THROUGH READING: Copy two of the following types of sentences directly from the reading. Be sure to include all punctuation and page numbers.

- description: find at least one sentence that describes a good image: setting, character(s), or an event. What makes it so descriptive? (analyze)

- a quotation.

- complete sentences.

- a sentence that includes a word that you did not know how to spell before this reading.

Literature Circles

Name _____ Date _____ Grade _____

Date	Page #	Title	Comments	Grade

Responding to Literature · Reader's-Writer's Reflections

WHO?

Upper-elementary, middle school, and high school students.

WHY?

Laura Truesdale knows that her eighth-graders are actively engaged with real literature because she hears them talking about their books in their literature study groups, recommending books to each other, and writing about books in their literature logs.

HOW?

Laura explains how she organizes for literature study: "My students are grouped around books they have chosen to read. Drawing on the books in my classroom library and the school library, we are able to accommodate all one hundred eighth-graders, using **Responding to Literature** to spark their ideas. Each day I give the students approximately thirty minutes to read, and at the end of the period we spend fifteen to twenty minutes talking about our books. I also ask them to work with their peers in small groups to represent their books visually in a web. In the final two days of the literature study groups, the students are given large sheets of newsprint, colored pens, and pencils, and they create their own webs based on what they think is most important in their books."

WHAT ELSE?

Maureen White also invites her students to explore their responses to their reading in writing. Using the **Reader's-Writer's Reflections** as a guideline, they write about every book they read.

READER'S-WRITER'S REFLECTIONS

What you write in this log should be what you want to remember about the books you will be reading this year. Suggested responses could be any thoughts, reactions, interpretations, or questions to what you are reading. You may want to record a quote or a special word and write why you liked it; you may want to write about how something in the book connects to your life; you may want to pose some questions that you would like to ask the author if that were possible; or you may want to compare one book with others you have read. Try to be aware of what makes it an effective or ineffective piece of writing. *PLEASE REMEMBER TO DATE ALL OF YOUR ENTRIES.*

See: MONITORING pp. 14, 20

Responding to Literature was developed by Laura S. Truesdale, an eighth-grade reading teacher at North Central High in Kershaw, SC, and a doctoral student and WRITE group teacher/consultant at the University of South Carolina.

Reader's-Writer's Reflections was developed by Maureen White, K–8 writing coordinator for Haverhill Public Schools in Haverhill, MA.

Responding to Literature

Name _____ Date _____ Grade _____

1. Title of book and author

2. Names of students in the group

3. Goals: number of pages to be read each day (you have seven days to read your book)

4. Make two predictions based on the cover and the synopsis on the back.

5. What is your initial reaction to your literature group?

6. Are you current with your goals?

7. Do you like your book so far? Why or why not?

8. Write three questions you have about your book and discuss them in your group.

9. Describe your web, including why you chose to include various components.

10. Final analysis; include your feelings about collaborating with your peers.

Author/Illustrator Study ·
Analyze an Author

WHO?

Elementary, middle school, and secondary students.

WHY?

There are many ways to become engaged with literature. Studying an individual author or illustrator provides one entry into the literary world.

HOW?

In order to conduct an **Author/Illustrator Study**, students need to read or view as many selections as possible by the same author or illustrator and then compare and contrast the individual selections. It might be interesting to compare the titles of an author who also illustrates his or her books to an author who doesn't.

In a similar way, to complete **Analyze an Author** students will need to locate and read as many of the author's works as possible.

WHAT ELSE?

Some whole language teachers invite their students to choose and present an author or illustrator to the whole class. Working alone or with a partner, students choose an author or illustrator to study, showcase his or her works in the classroom library, and display accompanying book posters and biographical information. Random House features biographical videos of such award-winning authors as Katherine Patterson and Cynthia Ryland; if possible, students might enjoy including these in their presentations. Over the course of the year, all students become familiar with a wide range of authors and illustrators.

See: INTERACTING p. 118

Author/Illustrator Study was developed by Debra Goodman, a fifth-grade teacher at the Dewey Learning Center in Detroit, MI.

Analyze an Author was developed by Toby Kahn Curry, an eighth-grade teacher also at the Dewey Learning Center .

Author/Illustrator Study on _____

Name _____   Date _____

TITLE	COPYRIGHT DATE	MEDIUM / MEDIA FOR ILLUSTRATION	CHARACTERS NAME / COMMENTS	PLOT

Analyze an Author

Name _____   Date _____

1. Select one of the author sets

2. Read the selections in the set

3. Think about the books in the set and then answer the following questions:

What ideas, themes, characters, or plots do you feel these books have in common?

What interesting or unusual things did you notice about the illustrations in the books?

In your opinion, does the author (or authors) have a certain message she/he is trying to communicate to her/his readers?

On a scale of 1 (low) to 10 (high), give this author a rating and a recommendation:

Book Review: Fiction Books / Non-Fiction Books / Picture Books · Listening Post Book Review

WHO?

Primary and upper-elementary school students.

WHY?

Book reviews allow students to think about the books they've read and to share them with others.

HOW?

Debra Goodman asks students to present at least one book to the class each month. One presentational option is to fill out a **Book Review** form (**Fiction**, **Non-Fiction**, or **Picture Books**). Mary Jo Regnier created the **Listening Post Book Review** forms, one for primary students and one for upper-elementary students to complete after listening to a story at the "listening post."

WHAT ELSE?

When students have a range of options for sharing a book with their peers, completing a book review can be enjoyable. The review is not just a way for the teacher to check up on students' reading (the traditional purpose for assigning book reports), but is an authentic way for students to share books they have read with a real audience of their peers.

See: INTERACTING p. 118

Book Review: Fiction Books / Non-Fiction Books / Picture Books was developed by Debra Goodman, a fifth-grade teacher at the Dewey Learning Center in Detroit, MI.

Listening Post Book Review was developed by Mary Jo Regnier, a teacher at Dewey Learning Center in Detroit, MI.

Book Review: Fiction Books

Name _____   Date _____

Title _____

Author _____

Number of pages _____

Tell what the book is about (briefly):

Retell your favorite part of the story:

What were some of the problems or issues in the story?

Would you recommend this book to a friend? Why or why not?

Overall rating:

Book Review: Non-Fiction Books

Name _____   Date _____

Title of book _____

Author _____

Number of pages _____

What did this book tell about?

What interesting things did you find out?

What especially surprised you about this topic?

Do you think the author did a good job of explaining the subject? Why or why not?

Would you recommend this book to a friend? Why or why not?

Book Review: Picture Books

(Use this form for a book that has pictures on every page)

Name _____   Date _____

Title of book _____

Author _____

Illustrator _____

What is this book about?

What was your favorite part of the book?

What medium did the illustrator use?

_____ crayon   _____ oil paint

_____ pencil   _____ water color

_____ pen and ink   _____ collage

_____ woodcuts   _____ chalks

_____ other:

Give your opinion of the illustrations:

Would you recommend this book to a friend? Why or why not?

Listening Post Book Review
(upper elementary)

Name _____

Date _____

Title of book _____

Author _____

Illustrator _____

My opinion of the story:

My opinion of the illustrations:

My opinion of the recording/telling:

Listening Post Book Review
(primary)

Name _____

Date _____

Title of book _____

Author _____

Illustrator _____

My opinion:

Here's a picture of my favorite part:

How Well Did We Work Together?

WHO?

Primary students.

WHY?

Diana Mazzuchi, Nancy Brooks, and Maggie Shine have developed a "process curriculum" in which they engage their students in cooperative groups to research something of their choice.

HOW?

They ask their students to follow a four-part process as they choose a topic to research, think about what they know about their chosen topic, and list questions they still have:

- What do we know about (topic of students' choice)?
- What do we want to know about the topic?
- How will we find out?
- How will we share what we know?

Each year they have a general theme under which students choose topics to research, while teaching thematically those topics for which they are held responsible by their district. Students work together in collaborative small research groups. After they have completed a project, they evaluate the process of their group work by filling out the form, **How Well Did We Work Together?**

WHAT ELSE?

Learning to collaborate with others requires sensitivity and flexibility. Students need to reflect on and monitor their collaborative learning experiences. Students will also benefit from designing their own group evaluation form.

See: REPORTING p. 206

How Well Did We Work Together? was developed by Diana Mazzuchi, Nancy Brooks, and Maggie Shine, teachers of a multi-grade 1,2,3 class in Brattleboro, VT.

How Well Did We Work Together?

Name _____   Date _____

1. I shared what I learned.

Not at all				Very much
1	2	3	4	5

2. I felt that my partners listened to me.

Not at all				Very much
1	2	3	4	5

3. I listened when my partners shared.

Not at all				Very much
1	2	3	4	5

4. I asked questions of my partners.

Not at all				Very much
1	2	3	4	5

5. I felt that our group worked well because:

_____

_____

_____

_____

6. Next time we can be more effective if we:

_____

_____

_____

_____

Self-Evaluation Across the Curriculum: Overview / Math / Science / Language Arts

WHO?

All elementary, middle school, and secondary students.

WHY?

Self-evaluation enables students to share what they know and to reflect again on what they have learned and how they have learned it.

HOW?

Debra Goodman explains how she involves her students in self-evaluation: "As a class, the students and I have more freedom to choose different topics, learning experiences, and materials since each child is responsible for recording his or her own progress. I involve students in every aspect of evaluation in my classroom, including report-card grades. At the end of the school year, I ask students to complete **Self-Evaluation Across the Curriculum** forms for the content area: **Language Arts**, **Social Studies**, **Science**, and a general **Overview**. I find the completed forms particularly revealing as I get the overall scope of each students' learning experiences across the curriculum. The forms also make filling out report cards easier. Because of their careful, thoughtful self-evaluations, students are not surprised when they get their report cards. They understand why and how the grades were determined, and they feel as though they've had a voice in the grading process."

WHAT ELSE?

"I learn so much more from open-ended, interactive evaluation that I can't imagine doing it any other way! The benefits to students and their parents are numerous as well; end-of-the-semester evaluation is no longer something to tolerate, but to learn from and grow."

See: OBSERVING p. 71; REPORTING pp. 175, 198, 200

Self-Evaluation Across the Curriculum forms were developed by Debra Goodman, who teaches fifth grade at the Dewey Learning Center in Detroit, MI.

Self-Evaluation Across the Curriculum: Overview

Name _____   Date _____

1. What are you proudest of this year?

2. How are you different than you were at the beginning of the school year?

3. What would you like to learn about next year?

4. What things did you like about this school year?

5. What things would you change or add for next year?

6. What grade would you give your teacher and why?

Self-Evaluation Across the Curriculum: Math

Name _____   Date _____

1. What do you enjoy most about math?

2. What have you learned about this year?

3. What do you feel you do best in math?

4. What would you like to learn more about next year?

Self-Evaluation Across the Curriculum: Science

Name _____   Date _____

Topics we studied _____

1. What activities did you participate with in the class science center?

2. List three interesting things that you learned.

3. What did you learn about how scientists find things out?

4. What books about science topics have you read this year?

5. What grade do you feel you should get in Science and why?

Self-Evaluation Across the Curriculum: Language Arts

Name _____ Date _____

1. List all of the books that you remember reading since the beginning of the school year. (Use the back of this page if necessary)

2. What is the best book you have read this year? Why?

3. Do you feel you have improved in your reading? Why or why not?

4. What would you like to improve about your reading?

5. What are you proudest of about your writing?

6. What would you like to improve?

Responding to Assignments: Self-Evaluation

WHO?

All students.

WHY?

Avery Walker gives her students the opportunity to evaluate their own work in all curriculum areas. **Responding to Assignments: Self-Evaluation** encourages children to think of their capabilities and focus on ways to have the quality of their work meet their potential.

HOW?

She keeps a box of these forms at the students' work station. Students need not complete a form for every assignment, but for those that require effort over an extended period of time, they know that the final step is to review their work and complete the form. If, in the process of review, they discover something that is amiss or not completed satisfactorily, they know they should take the time to revise and polish it.

WHAT ELSE?

Students revisit this form as they prepare to tackle a new project, recalling their self-evaluation. This experience helps students measure their own progress and assess the appropriateness of their self-selected goals.

See: REPORTING p. 193

Responding to Assignments: Self-Evaluation was developed by Avery Walker, a first/second-grade teacher at Ohlone School in Palo Alto, CA.

Responding to Assignments: Self-Evaluation

Name _____   Date _____

Type of assignment -

Title of assignment -

1. Did you try your hardest on this assignment?   ☐ YES   ☐ NO

2. Did you have to rush to complete this assignment?   ☐ YES   ☐ NO

3. How could you improve on this assignment?

4. I feel _____ about this assignment because

5. Goal: On my next assignment I am going to

Fostering Student Self-Evaluation: Focus on Writing

WHO?

Third grade through high school.

WHY?

This self-evaluation system fosters a dialogue between Bonnie Raines and each student, enabling her to feel as though she has her fingers on the pulse of each child's thinking. It also helps students develop their metacognition, providing a window into their thinking.

HOW?

Bonnie explains how she involves her students in self-evaluation: "Each day I collect work from four students in alphabetical order. An arrow on a chart identifies which four students are to hand in the following: (1) literature log, (2) free reading, (3) writing folder, and (4) math strategy book. I ask each student to include in both the literature log and the math strategy booklet a paragraph or so of self-assessment. In reading over literature responses they have written, I ask them to tell me what they consider the best example of their thinking. Is it a silent conversation they wrote with a partner? Is it a quick-write? A graphic symbol? Why? Are they putting forth their best effort in literature response? They also do a self-assessment in the math strategy booklet. I don't ask them to self-assess their writing at this time, because each month they select a piece for their writing portfolio and complete **Fostering Student Self-Evaluation: Focus on Writing**, explaining their reasons for their selection.

WHAT ELSE?

"I respond to the content of students' literature logs and math strategy booklets in the margins or at the bottom of pages. I draw a line and write the date where I left off so that the next time I see a student's work, I'll know where to resume responding. I also ask students to respond to at least two of my responses from the last time I read their work. This encourages them to read what I have written. I might ask them *why* they thought something, or to tell me more about an idea. They may have ten or twelve responses from me, so it is up to the students to pick two to answer. Though students orally share their literature and math thinking with each other, I like them to write more responses to each other so that I am not their primary audience."

See: REPORTING p. 193

Fostering Student Self-Evaluation: Focus on Writing was developed by Bonnie Raines, who teaches a fourth-fifth-sixth combination class at Proctor Terrace Elementary School in Santa Rosa, CA.

Fostering Student Self-Evaluation: Focus on Writing

Name _____   Date _____

Title _____

Genre _____

Reason for choosing this piece as an example of your best writing:

_____

_____

_____

_____

_____

_____

In what ways did you revise this piece?

_____

_____

_____

_____

What areas would you like to focus on for your next piece?

_____

_____

_____

With whom did you conference about this piece?

_____   _____   _____

Something to Write Home About

WHO?

Upper-elementary, middle school, and high school students.

WHY?

Phyllis Whitin explains how she involves her students in **Something to Write Home About**: "After writing conferences at the end of each school quarter, I ask my seventh-grade students to compose a letter to their parents. I have three purposes in mind: to maintain ties with parents, to encourage students to reflect upon their writing strategies and accomplishments, and to help students visualize future goals.

HOW?

"I find it interesting to see what students choose to include in their letters about their development as writers. Several students have commented on their attitude toward writing. Others highlighted what they considered to be the most important features of a writing workshop. Students described the goals from the previous quarter as well as those that they had set for the next quarter during conference time. For the second round of letters, I ask students to add an additional paragraph. I ask them to invite their parents to write a response to the students' letter or about seventh grade in general. I want the students to feel recognized and to have a tangible record of their parents' ideas. Parents comment on both their child's accomplishments and their feelings about their child's progress.

"The students and parents have written and shared. Through reading their letters, I, too, have come to understand both the strategies and the feelings of my students. I appreciate them in their roles as family members. Borrowing the words from a student's letter, I feel 'I have learned uncountable new things.'"

WHAT ELSE?

Christina Althoff asks her students to write home twice a year, describing to their parents both the academic and social aspects of their school experiences. In this way, parents receive rich information from their child about what is working well for them, what they like and feel good about, as well as those things on which they need to spend more time working. The letter is addressed to both the teacher and parents. The student, who attends the twice-yearly parent-teacher conference, opens the conference by reading his or her letter aloud to Christina and his or her parents. A sample letter written by a sixth-grade student appears on the adjacent page.

See: REPORTING p. 216

Something to Write Home About was developed by Phyllis Whitin, seventh-grade language arts teacher at Irmo Middle School, Campus R, in Columbia, SC, and Christina Althoff, sixth-grade teacher at Jane Lathrop Stanford Middle School in Palo Alto, CA.

Something to Write Home About

(sample letter)

DEAR Mom and Mrs. Althoff:

Thank you for coming to my conference. In this letter I'm going to tell you about my feelings and my progress in school.

I have many things in school that I like doing. I like reading and I love writing. I like math when I understand it. I think I have improved in reading. We are studying geology and I really like that. I like almost everything in school. I need to improve in my spelling. I really need help in my spelling because I feel I can't write without someone correcting it all the time. I feel I am limited in how much I can write because of my spelling.

We learned a lot in math so far. We have been doing a lot of group projects and I really like that. We also have been doing Problems of the Week in math and that is ok. I really like math when I understand it, but when I don't I get really frustrated. I think I need help in division and some multiplication.

We have been doing science, too. First we did astronomy and we started working on posters but never finished it. Now we are doing geology and that is fun. We are doing posters. My group is doing the Cenozoic Era. When we finish we are going to give a presentation to room 41.

We do a lot of reading in my room. We get to read almost every day. I really like reading and I love it when we do have time to read in the classroom. I think I have improved in reading since last year. The books that we have been reading in our classroom are just right. I like talking about the book in groups because I get to tell about how I feel about what's going on in the book and I get to hear what other people think about it, too. We have to read 300 pages every month and I think that is good. Reading that much every month is just right for me.

We don't do as much writing as I wish we would. I love writing and we have not been doing much of it. We have been writing a little on the computers and that's fine with me. I'd rather write by hand because I can write faster by hand than by computer. But I would like to do free writing and not have to write on a certain topic that I may not know much about or care about.

In social studies we have been talking about the election. I'm glad we talk about it because this election is very important because it's a close race. No one can possibly tell who is going to win. We are always able to vote and I'm glad we talk about the election because someday we are going to vote.

When I came to J.L.S. I only had a few friends because most of my friends are going to Jordan. But after about a week I had made new friends. Now I'm very close to them. I think I'm doing O.K. in school. I try very hard to get my work in on time. I think I'm good with planning my time so everything gets in on time. When I turn something in I make sure it's my very best.

(signed)

Thinking About Myself as a Learner

WHO?

Toby Kahn Curry developed this for her sixth/seventh-grade class; accordingly, it reflects her curriculum and instructional strategies. Teachers of any grade level can create similar forms that reflect their classroom learning experiences and achieve a similar purpose: helping students reflect on and evaluate their own learning.

WHY?

The most effective learners are often those who can step outside of their learning and examine what has worked for them, what hasn't, and how they might revise their strategies to become more successful. A simple form like **Thinking About Myself as a Learner** helps students reflect on their own learning. It also provides teachers with invaluable insights into their students' experiences and the meanings they have created and drawn from the curriculum for themselves. Finally, teachers demonstrate their belief in and respect for their students as capable and creative learners. Together, as learning partners, they evaluate and revise the classroom learning experiences as needed.

HOW?

Toby's students complete this form at the end of each semester. During the parent-student-teacher conferences, the forms are reviewed to examine how students are progressing, what they have found meaningful, and what they plan to do next.

WHAT ELSE?

Based on a review of the end-of-semester forms and with teacher assistance, students might write up a learning plan in which they outline for themselves how they might revise their work strategies to make more productive use of their classroom learning time.

See: REPORTING pp. 193, 198, 200, 212

Student Self-Evaluation was developed by Toby Kahn Curry, a middle school teacher at the Dewey Center for Urban Education in Detroit, MI.

Thinking About Myself as a Learner

Name _____ Date _____ Grade _____

Please write thoughtful, honest answers for this evaluation. Remember, you are the best source for evaluating your own learning. Only you know what you knew before the school year started, and only you know how much you've learned in the last 20 weeks. I have made many observations about each of you as learners, but your response on this form is invaluable. Please use lined paper to answer any questions that require additional space.

1. Describe the most important thing that you learned or accomplished in your research.

2. Describe what and how much you have read so far this year.

3. Explain what kind of math you have worked on.

4. Describe the different kinds of writing you have done so far this school year.

5. How do you like working in collaborative groups with your classmates?

6. What assignments or experiences did you most enjoy this school year?

7. What did you least enjoy about the first semester?

8. If you could change something about the way our room is organized, what would it be?

9. How do you hope to improve upon your learning during the second semester?

Weekly Discussion Group Evaluation · Evaluation of Discussion Groups · Evaluation of Group Projects

WHO?

Upper-elementary, middle school, and high school students.

WHY?

In order to find out how his students are progressing on their various projects, Howard Miller has developed a number of response forms.

HOW?

Howard explains how he uses the forms: "The first two forms, **Weekly Discussion Group Evaluation** and **Evaluation of Discussion Groups**, deal with our weekly literature discussion groups. The third form, **Evaluation of Group Projects**, is used when the students are working on a big-group project. The students are given opportunities to assign grades to themselves and to each other. I exercise my own judgment when it comes to grades, but I have found that we agree more often than not. They know when they have done a good job.

WHAT ELSE?

"As time has passed, I have given my students more and more responsibilities. We still have lots of projects throughout the year, but I no longer dictate the content or format for them. Instead, I have learned to give them the leeway to develop their own projects, work out their own processes, and solve their own problems—sometimes alone, sometimes with a partner, sometimes with a group. My major role is that of facilitator, strategist, someone to bounce ideas off of. I supply the books, the paper, the journals, the pencils, the crayons, and the posterboard. They supply the creativity and sweat, and they take much of the responsibility for their own learning."

See: REPORTING p. 191

Weekly Discussion Group Evaluation, Evaluation of Discussion Groups, and Evaluation of Group Projects were developed by Howard M. Miller, a reading and English teacher at Jefferson Junior High School, Jefferson City, MO.

Weekly Discussion Group Evaluation

Name _____ Date _____

1. What good things happened in today's discussion?

2. Were there any problems with the discussion today?

3. What did you do to help your group today?

4. How can you help improve the discussion next time?

5. Based on your comments, what grade do you think you should get for your discussion today?

Evaluation of Discussion Groups

Name _____   Date _____

1. What do you think is the purpose of discussion groups?

2. Do you think having discussions about books is a useful activity? Explain.

3. Have you learned anything from your discussion group? Explain.

4. Have you ever chosen a book after hearing someone talk about it in discussion group? If so, explain.

5. Who usually are your partners when we have discussion groups?

6. Do you think it would be useful to work with other partners sometimes? Explain.

7. How careful have you been in filling out the Weekly Discussion Group Evaluation form after the discussions?

8. Do you like the idea of giving yourself a grade? Do you think you do a good job of giving yourself a grade?

9. Do you think we should continue to have discussion groups? Explain.

Evaluation of Group Projects

Name _____   Date _____

1. What has been your contribution to the project so far?

2. Who has done the most work in your group so far?

3. Are there any problems that your group needs to work on?

4. Do you think you will need my help? Explain.

5. How much time does your group spend working on the project each day? Does your group use its time wisely? Explain.

6. Based on your view of everyone's work so far, what grade would you assign your group? Why?

7. What grade would you assign yourself? Why?

Learning How to Learn a Second Language

WHO?

High school or college students who are learning a second language.

WHY?

The evaluation of student progress in Mark Caprio's classes is a collaborative effort between the students and the teacher. **Learning How to Learn a Second Language** is his interpretation of what Rogers (1969) calls "learning how to learn"; a basic requirement of the educated person.

HOW?

Self-reflection and self-evaluation are conducted in three different ways: short term, long term, or at the end of the year. *Short-term* reflection and evaluations are conducted after the discussion period every week. Non-English majors, whose classes meet once a week, complete a chart indicating the percentage they spoke in English (as opposed to Japanese) and the general topic of their discussion. English majors, whose classes meet three times a week, have a thirty-minute discussion period once a week. Students keep notebooks in which they record their successes and failures, disappointments and satisfactions experienced during the discussion period. They answer these questions: (1) What did you talk about? (2) Are you satisfied with your speaking today? Why or why not? (3) List any problems you had while talking. (4) Give yourself a grade for today's conversation class. English majors also keep a chart noting the percentage of English they spoke.

Long-term reflection and evaluation sessions are held four times a year. The evaluation questionnaires ask students to evaluate their efforts and progress in the English language over the quarter and to comment to the class. Students are asked to write down the names of books they have read and the number of pages they have written in their exchange journals. Students also write an essay comparing their English ability at the beginning of the school year with the end.

The *end-of-year* reflection and evaluation session consists of two steps. In the first step, students write down the grade they believe they earned over the year and why they feel they deserve it. The second step involves a five- to ten-minute discussion with each student about his or her grade.

WHAT ELSE?

Self-reflection and evaluation is a process that all teachers must undertake in order to become more effective. Mark explains that he hopes "to continue in my search for ways in which my students and I can improve our learning as well as our understanding of the processes of learning."

Reference
Rogers, C. 1969. *Freedom to Learn*. Columbus, OH: Charles
    E. Merrill.

See: ANALYZING p. 141

Learning How to Learn a Second Language was developed by Mark Caprio while he was an instructor at Nanzan University in Nagoya, Japan. He is now a graduate student in Asian Studies at the University of Washington, Seattle.

Learning How to Learn a Second Language

Name _____   Date _____

1. List all that you have written: title, draft (first, second draft, final copy, etc.).

2. List all that you have read.

Title	Type of reading	# of pages

3. Free writing.   Week   1   2   3   4   5   6

     # of words   ___   ___   ___   ___   ___   ___

4. Write about any problems you are having when you read/write.

5. Write about your group (good points and bad points).

6. Do you notice any improvement in your reading/writing? Explain.

7. When I read in English I feel _____ because …

8. When I write in English I feel _____ because …

9. How many pages have you written in your journal? _____ pages

10. How can the class be made better for you?

Self-Evaluation in a Graduate Course

WHO?

Toby Kahn Curry and Debra Goodman have team-taught a course in whole language at Wayne State University for the past three years. Most of the students are full-time teachers working on their master's degree; however, this form would work in a graduate course or professional development institute.

WHY?

Debra and Toby explain: "In our course, evaluation is a natural outgrowth of the learning that takes place in the course. The teachers are trusted to learn, to work hard, and to evaluate their own progress through description or demonstration.

HOW?

"First, we have a set of open-ended expectations. The students are expected to keep a reflective journal responding to presentations, discussions, and readings. They participate in a literature study group focusing on a professional book. They select three to five inquiry questions to study throughout the semester. And they may participate in a thematic study group to support their inquiry research.

"Final 'products' are very process oriented. We ask our graduate students to maintain records of their readings and other work time, such as classroom visits or interviews. We don't ask for formal reports, but we ask that students write a few pages in response to each of their inquiry questions at the end of the semester. These responses should not be heavily dosed with quotes from other people, but should reflect the teacher's current thinking about the inquiry question.

"Each student is involved in two presentations. The literature groups are asked to give a creative 'book talk' to the class. The other presentation is even more open-ended. Students can present in groups or alone, focusing on some part of their learning that they would like to share with the class.

"The journals provide us with a window into how the students are doing and allow the students to complain or ask questions that they might not want to say out loud. We have a take-home mid-term, asking students to give progress reports on their readings and course activities. We also ask the students to suggest mid-term questions, and then have them respond to two of these questions. We have each student fill out **Self-Evaluation in a Graduate Course**, and use finals' week for fifteen-minute evaluation conferences with each student.

WHAT ELSE?

"Teacher/graduate students can learn a lot about whole language teaching through presentations, reading, personal inquiry, and group study. Yet they learn just as much about teaching through observing their own learning process in the class. It is important that college courses be process oriented, and evaluation holistic in nature."

See: REPORTING p. 204

Self-Evaluation in a Graduate Course was developed by Toby Kahn Curry, an eighth-grade teacher, and Debra Goodman, a fifth-grade teacher, at the Dewey Center for Urban Education, Detroit, MI.

Self-Evaluation in a Graduate Course

Name _____   Date _____

Please turn this in along with:

    a. your inquiry answers

    b. a bibliography of your readings

    c. your journal

1. What have you learned that has contributed most to your own professional growth?

2. Comment on your class participation (discussion, small groups, etc.).

3. Comment on your actual work and effort put into this class.

4. Are you satisfied with your inquiry questions and responses?

5. What class experience(s) did you find most useful?

6. What would you change if you were the course instructor?

7. Grade request:

   Instructor agree?

Teacher Self-Evaluation

WHO?

All teachers.

WHY?

The **Teacher Self-Evaluation** is given to all teachers at the Sonoma County Day School to help them in the process of self-evaluation. Teaching is a continual process of self-reflection and revision; teachers, like students, need to think about what is working well for them, what is not working as well, and what they can do to become more effective, responsive educators.

HOW?

Anne Seil explains, "I feel it is a nonthreatening form and encourages thinking and accountability. It is used during performance evaluation as a springboard to discussion. There's something about putting it in writing that encourages one to really work at improving and making it happen."

WHAT ELSE?

Teachers might enjoy and benefit from sharing their completed forms together as a faculty. In this way, they can identify professional goals they share as a faculty as well as their individual learning goals. Just as we strive to create learning communities in our classrooms with our students, so we want to build a professional learning community with our colleagues. The hallmark of a true professional may well be a commitment to continual learning. Effective schools are those in which teachers are continually reflecting on, evaluating, extending, and refining their professional knowledge and practices.

See: OBSERVING p. 90

Teacher Self-Evaluation was developed by Anne B. Seil and Pat Marchand, teachers at Sonoma County Day School in Santa Rosa, CA.

Teacher Self-Evaluation

Name _____   Date _____

GOOD AT	WORKING ON

GOALS: 3 YEARS

Semester Update · Parent Response Form

WHO?

Toby Kahn Curry developed **Semester Update** for her sixth/seventh-grade class. It reflects her curriculum and instructional strategies. Teachers of any grade level can write a similar letter explaining to their students' families their educational philosophies and the curricular and instructional strategies they have developed to support that philosophy.

WHY?

Education should be a shared endeavor between home and school. Teachers who send letters home throughout the school year not only keep their students' families informed of classroom developments and learning experiences, but equally important, make it clear that they value their partnership with the families. Furthermore, many parents like to participate in the classroom; by specifically outlining the sorts of help needed, teachers such as Toby open the door to parent involvement.

HOW?

Toby sends detailed letters home at least three times a year, at the beginning and end of each semester.

WHAT ELSE?

Based on a review of the forms she receives back from parents, she knows what their needs, concerns, and questions are and she can respond accordingly.

See: REPORTING p. 202

Semester Update and Parent Response Form were developed by Toby Kahn Curry, an eighth-grade teacher at the Dewey Center for Urban Education in Detroit, MI.

Semester Update

(sample letter)

DEAR PARENTS,

Here at semester break time the kids and I would like to give you an update for the next semester as well as an evaluation of the first semester. So far, we've had a good year growing and learning together. The class has come together as a community of learners, and our conflicts are being resolved in a more humane matter. I am beginning to see more spontaneous collaboration during work time. This is a very important class accomplishment.

We finished our first major research project, our "I-Search" work, last semester. The sixth-graders became experts on one country in the world and the seventh-graders researched a topic in American history from the 1600s to the 1800s. Almost everyone completed this very complicated, sophisticated, and realistic research process. The oral presentations of their research were exceptional. Please make sure you let your child know how proud you are that he or she completed this project.

Another big success last semester was our college pen pal exchange with students at Macomb Community College. This was a weekly writing project that everybody participated in, and it was a wonderful way for us to share school experiences with students from another community and age group. Many of the kids are still communicating with their pen pals from last semester We have also written to pen pals of the same age in Madison, Wisconsin, and Harlem, New York. These real-life writing experiences are invaluable. Another ongoing writing experience is being facilitated every Tuesday with the help of one of our parents, Marjorie Harnois (Taj's mom). Each Tuesday, two students accompany Ms. Harnois to the St. Patrick's Senior Center where they are interviewing senior citizens and writing a book on folk remedies. This cross-age experience has been wonderful for our children as they learn about the early lives of these senior citizens.

The other regular classroom activities that we have participated in include Middle School Math Concepts, personal journals, weekly current events, social studies log books, National Geographic videos, individual self-selected and personal reading journals, and literature/genre discussion groups.

This coming semester we will be participating in the same regular classroom activities as we undertake two new thematic units "Everyday is Earthday" and "The Struggle for Equal Rights." We will enlarge our research by viewing the following documentaries and films:

1. "Eyes on the Prize," Series 1
2. "Roots," Parts 1–6
3. "And the Children Shall Lead," a Wonderworks film about voting rights
4. "Glory," a Civil War film
5. "The Civil War: The Cause," a PBS documentary
6. "Fat Man and Little Boy," a film about the atom bomb in WWII
7. "The Grapes of Wrath," a film about the Great Depression
8. "To Kill a Mockingbird," a film about racism in the American south
9. "All God's Children," a film about busing in urban America
10. "A Dry White Season," a film about apartheid in South Africa
11. "Gorillas in the Mist," a film about animal rights
12. "Mississippi Burning," a film about racism in the American south
13. "The Dollmaker," a film about a famous Appalachian woman.

We will discuss each documentary as we build our understanding of the struggle for equal rights in America and around the world. We will be viewing these films over a period of nineteen weeks. I will preview each film and each student will use her/his log book for responses to the content. The whole class will also be hearing the books *Sorrow's Kitchen*, a biography of Zora N. Hurston, and *All Times, All People: A World History of Slavery*, by Milton Meltzer.

Attached to this letter you will find your child's self-evaluation for the first semester. Please read it carefully and discuss it with your child.

Please feel free to write me a response to this letter. I would love to know how you view your child's involvement in school this year. In general, it has been a pleasure as well as a challenge to work with your children.

Sincerely,
Ms. Curry

HOW PARENTS CAN HELP

1. We need help getting our class quilt published. Can you sew? Can you donate money for fabric and materials?
2. We need markers, tape, writing stationery, envelopes, stamps, and spiral or sewn notebooks for our many classroom projects. Can you donate these items or funds to purchase them?
3. We send out monthly book orders; please encourage your child to purchase at least one book a month to build her/his own personal home library.

Thanks for your time and consideration.

- -

PARENT RESPONSE FORM
(Return this sheet with your child's report card)

Yes, we have read the midterm evaluation packet that you have sent home with my child's second report card. We will contact you if we can help with the class projects or donate any supplies to the room.

DATE_____

STUDENT SIGNATURE _____

PARENT SIGNATURE _____

Comments or Suggestions:

RETURN THIS FORM ALONG WITH YOUR CHILD'S REPORT CARD PRINTOUT

Getting Started with Portfolios

WHO?

All teachers, administrators, parents, and students.

WHY?

Individual teachers, schools, and districts are turning to portfolios as an authentic representation of the depth and breadth of students' developing knowledge and ability.

HOW?

The most effective use of portfolios begins with careful consideration of a range of issues surrounding their design and practice. A checklist such as **Getting Started with Portfolios** can guide your thinking-through process. Following the lead of Tierney, Carter, and Desai (1991), here's one possible way to put portfolios into practice:

- The criteria for assessment and portfolio development are ideally negotiated and agreed upon between students and teachers; parents may also be invited to state their educational goals for their children and these are incorporated as well.

- Students begin to build and organize portfolios, using the agreed upon criteria for item selection and self-evaluation. Students may include a self-evaluation form with each selected piece indicating why they chose the piece and what it reveals about their abilities as readers, writers, or learners, or they can write a brief statement noting the same points.

- At the end of the grading period, students review their portfolios and write an evaluative summary detailing what they view as their strengths and future goals ("Things I Do Well, Things I Am Working On, Things I Plan to Learn"). The summary and portfolio are submitted to the teacher.

- The teacher conducts an evaluative conference with each student (parents may be included, too), and together they review the portfolio and the student's self-evaluative comments and summary. The teacher shares his or her assessment of the portfolio, and together the student and teacher agree upon the goals the student should focus on next and how to go about achieving them.

- The teacher then writes a narrative summary of the conference and what his or her curricular and instructional strategies are for the student.

WHAT ELSE?

There is more than one way to use portfolios. Allow yourself and your students time to experiment.

Reference

Tierney, J. R., Carter, M. A., and Desai, L. E. 1991. *Portfolio assessment in the reading-writing classroom*. Norwood, MA : Christopher-Gordon.

See: OBSERVING p. 93; ANALYZING p. 145

Getting Started with Portfolios was developed by Lois Bridges Bird.

Getting Started with Portfolios

1. What is the purpose for the portfolio?
—— Will students include work in their portfolios from across the curriculum? Or focus primarily on the language arts?

—— Will students include finished products only? Or will they include the process of their work as well as the finished product so that a range of response is evident; drafts of written compositions as well as the final, polished piece?

—— Will they include best work only or projects that didn't work as well?

—— Will the portfolio serve your class only, or will you pass it on to the student's next-year teacher?

—— Will the portfolios serve the school? the district?

—— How exactly will the portfolios be shared?

2. Who will contribute to the portfolio?
—— Will students select and control exclusively the contents of the portfolios?

—— Will you as the teacher also have the right to make selections?

—— Will parents be invited to contribute?

3. How will you establish criterion for portfolio development?
—— What criteria will you use for selecting the material that goes in the portfolio?

—— Will you establish the criteria?

—— Will you negotiate criteria with your students?

—— Will parents have input?

—— Do you need to follow district or state evaluative guidelines?

4. What will you use as a portfolio?
Portfolios can take many forms. Which will you choose? Will you require a uniform format or let each student design his or her own? Listed below are some possibilities:

—— accordion file

—— three-hole ring binder

—— 8$\frac{1}{2}$" by 11" manila folder

—— specially designed oversized, cardboard folder

—— commercial portfolio

—— large boot box

5. What will students include in their portfolios?
This can be completely open-ended, limited only by the physical dimensions of the portfolio and storage constraints. Here is a list of possible inclusions:

—— questions, issues, brainstorming, notes associated with research projects

—— sketches, semantic maps

—— photographs

—— rough drafts, works in progress

—— published books

—— completed theme cycles

—— peer and teacher feedback

—— reflection on peer and teacher feedback

—— writing samples

_____ lists of books the student has read
_____ comments from student about the books
_____ who the student shared the books with
_____ audiotapes of the student reading; may record reading once a month,
and include the student's self-evaluation of the reading
_____ miscue analysis
_____ literature logs
_____ lists of literature studies in which the student has participated
_____ descriptions of reading and writing strategies the student controls
_____ lists of writing conventions the student controls
_____ personal reactions to classroom experiences
_____ self-evaluations.

6. How will students review and add to their portfolios?
_____ Will students review and add to their portfolios whenever they are inspired to do so?
_____ Will you schedule a regular time for selection and review? How frequently?
Once a week? Every two weeks? Once a month? End of the semester?
_____ Will you review portfolios as a whole class activity or meet with
small groups of students or individuals?

7. Self-evaluation format:
Self-evaluation is the key component of portfolio assessment. How will you
engage students in self-evaluation?
_____ Will you ask them to write a self-evaluative paragraph for each entry explaining
why they chose to include the entry and what it shows about their developing ability?
_____ Will you develop a form that they complete and clip to each entry?

8. How will you evaluate the portfolio?
What criteria will you use? Here is a list you might consider:
_____ evidence of the student's risk-taking
_____ flexibility as a language user: writing and reading fluency across genre and function
_____ revising, editing, and experimenting with different literacy modes
_____ ability to refine and elaborate upon meaning (skills/conventions)
_____ awareness of own thinking
_____ ability to pose questions
_____ ability to find answers to questions and use a variety of resources
_____ self-reflection on teacher and student feedback
_____ self-assessment; ability to step outside of learning experience
and reflect on one's language and thought

9. Goal-setting:
Portfolios may be most effective when the teacher can meet with each student
and discuss the contents of the portfolio. What is the student learning? What is
working well? What isn't working as well? What direction should the
student take next?
_____ Will you set the curricular and instructional goals for the student?
_____ Will you negotiate the goals with the student?
_____ Will parents have a say in setting goals for their child?

Portfolio Evenings: Guiding Questions

WHO?

First- through eighth-grade students and their parents.

WHY?

Encouraged by the kinds of thinking that children had expressed in their written student reflections on our Learning Experiences Form (see page 224), the Crow Island School faculty realized that they were capable of much more. Getting them more involved in the process of assessment made sense.

HOW?

Every student has a portfolio that represents work across all domains. Students maintain their portfolios all year and frequently have conferences with the teacher about works in progress, additions, and deletions. At the end of the year, their portfolios are combined with past years' work and stored in the student archives. The archives are alphabetically arranged in open shelving in the resource center along with historical documents, publications, and photographs of the school and students.

In preparation for portfolio evenings, the teacher divides the class into small groups of six or seven at the primary level (larger groups at grade four and five) and assigns a night for each group of students and their parents. Children review their portfolio/archive as teachers guide them with reflective questions such as those found in **Portfolio Evenings: Guiding Questions**.

The idea is to ask guiding questions that help children reflect on their learning. Students are encouraged to write about their learning and to include these thoughts as part of their portfolios. Developing the metacognitive process in students, even at a young age, heightens their awareness and commitment to a critical assessment of their learning.

WHAT ELSE?

On Portfolio Evenings, which last for about an hour and a half, the children sit with their parents and present their portfolios. The teacher and principal circulate, visiting each student and highlighting particular milestones that each youngster may have attained. They are available for questions but try not to intrude, because it is really the children's evening, and they need to run the show as much as possible. Parents and teachers have been impressed with the leadership and independence that even the youngest students have demonstrated in this setting.

— Adapted from "Portfolios Invite Reflection—from Students and Staff" (*Educational Leadership*, May 1992, pp. 58–61).

See: OBSERVING p. 93; ANALYZING p. 145; REPORTING pp. 224, 235

Portfolio Evenings: Guiding Questions was developed by Elizabeth A. Hebert, principal of Crow Island School in Winnetka, IL.

Portfolio Evenings: Guiding Questions

Name _____ Date _____ Grade _____

1. How has your writing changed since last year (or since September?)

2. What do you know about math now that you didn't know in September?

3. Let's compare a page from a book you were reading last year and a book you are reading now and include copies of each in your portfolio.

4. What is unique about your portfolio?

5. What would you like Mom and Dad to understand about your portfolio? Can you organize it so it will show that?

Learning Experiences Form

WHO?

First-grade through eighth-grade students and their parents.

WHY?

The Crow Island School faculty was dissatisfied and frustrated with mandated standardized modes of assessment. Standardized tests did not reflect the way they taught, the effects of their teaching on children, nor how they adapted instruction to individual learners. They wanted to describe children's learning experiences to parents in ways that:

- authentically describe the child
- address issues of accountability and maintain the integrity of their beliefs about children and how they learn
- reflect the different ways that teachers organize instruction
- provide concrete information compatible with parents' expectations

HOW?

Influenced by Howard Gardner's *Frames of Mind* (1983), they designed the **Learning Experiences Form** so that it reflects the multiple dimensions of a child's learning. They also designated space for the student's self-reflection about his or her learning. Older students write their own thoughts; teachers take dictation for the first-graders. Teachers and students complete this form at the end of both fall and spring semesters.

WHAT ELSE?

On the back of the form they include a curriculum overview. A series of mini-statements explain curriculum objectives for that portion of the year. They have also begun to include parents' thoughts about their child's learning experiences in the assessment form.

— Adapted from "Portfolios Invite Reflection—from Students and Staff" (*Educational Leadership*, May 1992, pp. 58–61).

Reference
Gardner, H. 1983. *Frames of mind: The theory of multiple intelligences*. New York: Basic Books.

See: OBSERVING p. 93; ANALYZING p. 145

Learning Experiences Form was contributed by Elizabeth A. Hebert, principal of Crow Island School in Winnetka, IL.

Learning Experiences Form

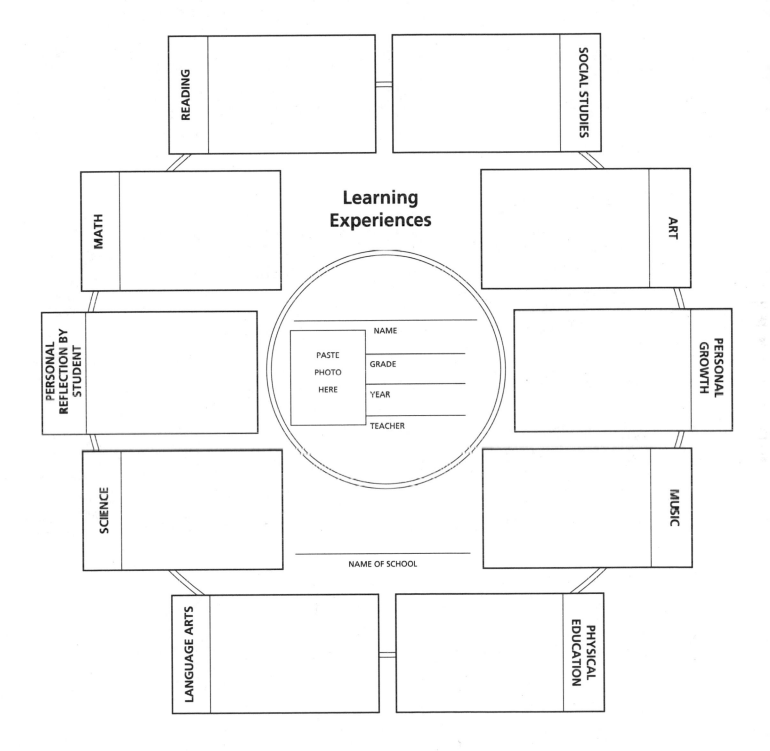

READING

SOCIAL STUDIES

MATH

ART

Learning Experiences

PERSONAL REFLECTION BY STUDENT

PERSONAL GROWTH

NAME

PASTE PHOTO HERE

GRADE

YEAR

TEACHER

SCIENCE

MUSIC

NAME OF SCHOOL

LANGUAGE ARTS

PHYSICAL EDUCATION

Portfolio Assessment: Self-Evaluation Sheet

WHO? _____

Third grade students through high school.

WHY? _____

The value of the portfolio lies less in its contents than in the self-evaluation it inspires. As students engage in self-assessment, portfolios become more than a collection of their best work; they invite students to become active participants in the learning process rather than passive recipients of grades.

HOW? _____

Betty-Ann Craven explains: "Students need to set goals and evaluate their own progress. My students start the year by setting goals for what they hope to accomplish during the year in each subject area, and they revise their goals quarterly. The revision of personal goals tells as much about student growth as the portfolio itself. Are the goals achievable, unrealistic, or not high enough?

"It is helpful to use actual student work to provide a model by which students can judge themselves. For instance, in writing, I use anonymous student samples from previous years to discuss the specifics of what makes a piece of writing good, mediocre, or poor. Then students have a realistic measure by which to judge their work. Asking students to be as specific as they can in goal-setting is crucial in helping them reach their goals.

"Along with the quarterly goal-setting, students complete a quarterly **Portfolio Assessment: Self-Evaluation Sheet** to help them organize and choose what should be included in their portfolios. Continual self-assessment by students benefits me as a teacher and the students as learners.

"Portfolios must contain one or two pieces of writing from students' writing folder that they think shows their growth as a writer. These compositions must include all the stages of the writing process, from brainstorming through first draft, to peer-editing sheets and the finished copy. Students must also include two pieces of writing from other content areas as well as evidence of problem-solving skills in either math or another subject area.

WHAT ELSE? _____

"Through self-assessment students are engaged and focused. They buy into the educational process in a way that isn't possible with traditional testing and evaluation procedures. Students come to realize that education is not something imposed on them by schools, parents, and teachers. Rather, they begin to see that what they do contributes to how they progress as learners. Self-evaluation instills a sense of responsibility that no lecture from a teacher or parent can match. That alone makes portfolios and self-assessment worth trying in your own classroom."

See: ANALYZING p. 145

Portfolio Assessment: Self-Evaluation Sheet was developed by Betty-Ann Craven, a fifth-grade teacher and reading specialist at Bollinger Canyon School in San Ramon, CA.

Portfolio Assesment: Self-Evaluation Sheet

Name _____ Date _____ Grade _____

1. List the areas or skills you have been studying. Be specific.

2. Describe how you think you are doing as a student in this class.
   Give the reasons why you think this.

3. Describe what you have learned so far in this class. This may include
   something you can do now that you couldn't do before.

4. Describe the areas where you need more work and explain why.

5. Additional comments.

Growth Portfolio Rationale · Quarterly Growth Summary

WHO?

Elementary school students.

WHY?

Lowell Elementary School has been actively working to create assessment procedures that reflect its child-centered, meaning-based philosophy of education.

HOW?

Students keep three portfolios:

1. The *working portfolio* is an accessible file including representative samples of daily work. It contains a large variety of work that is frequently reviewed by teachers and students to select pieces for the growth portfolio.

2. The *growth portfolio* contains authentic text that demonstrates student growth. This portfolio may contain quarterly progress reports; growth assessments; student self-evaluations; reading logs; interest inventories; writing, math, and thematic study samples; and parent feedback. The growth portfolio is returned to students when they leave the school.

3. The *progress folder* is easily accessible to students and teachers. It is constantly updated and revised. Its purpose is to provide ease, organization, and accessibility to growth and assessment information. The progress folder is passed on to the child's next teacher and contains a quarterly growth assessment form, weekly assignment schedule, portfolio rationale forms, student schedules, and anecdotal progress notes.

WHAT ELSE?

Teachers, parents, and students all can contribute to the growth portfolio. When they choose an item for the portfolio, they complete and clip to the item a **Growth Portfolio Rationale** form. The **Quarterly Growth Summary** is completed by the teacher and student during an individual student-teacher evaluation conference. Together they review the student's work in writing, reading, math, and thematic projects, and negotiate the student's academic goals for the next quarter.

See: OBSERVING p. 93

Growth Portfolio Rationale and Quarterly Growth Summary were developed by Lowell Elementary School primary grade teachers Kathleen Cain, Cathy Carter, Nycki Guest, Jan Haddick, Rose Hammond, Kay Keeley, and Carol Munier in Missoula, MT.

Growth Portfolio Rationale

Name _____ Date _____ Grade _____

Title of work _____

List the reasons why this piece of work will become a part of the Growth Portfolio.

STUDENT

_____

_____

_____

Signature _____

TEACHER

_____

_____

_____

Signature _____

PARENT

_____

_____

_____

Signature _____

Quarterly Growth Summary

Name _____ Date _____ Grade _____

Key: D = Developing   I = Independent

WRITING

Goals   Comments

_____

_____

_____

_____

_____

READING

Goals   Comments

_____

_____

_____

_____

_____

MATH

Goals   Comments

_____

_____

_____

_____

THEMATIC

Goals   Comments

_____

_____

_____

_____

My Child as a Language Learner, K–6

WHO?

Elementary school students and their parents.

WHY?

Palo Alto Unified School District has long recognized that parents are often children's first and best teachers. Accordingly, they developed **My Child as a Language Learner** to further support the home-school connection.

HOW?

Teachers may use the forms in any way that best suits their educational needs. Kindergarten teacher Kate Calfee has parents complete the form at the parent-teacher conference. She then initials the items she believes characterize the child. Any discrepancy between her opinion and parents' opinions becomes an opportunity for discussion. In this way she is able to utilize parental input as she strives to create a curricular and instructional school experience that will best support each child as an individual learner with unique needs and abilities.

WHAT ELSE?

Parents almost always respond favorably to school forms that invite them to share information about their child. Such forms immediately signal to parents the school's commitment to working closely with them. Parents feel as though they have a voice in their child's education and can join with the school to create a rich learning experience for the child.

See: MONITORING p. 20; INTERACTING p. 127; ANALYZING p. 141

My Child as a Language Learner, K–6, was developed by Marianne Jones, Wendla Dyer, Rena Malkofsky, Carolyn Richard, and Julie Ryan, Language Arts Committee, Palo Alto Unified School District, Palo Alto, CA.

My Child as a Language Learner
Parent Observation (Grades K–1)

Child's Name _____ Date _____ Grade _____

Please tell us about your child's language learning in the following areas. Please feel free to comment. We appreciate your insights as we work together with your child.

My Child:	Usually	Some-times	Rarely	Comments
1. Speaks clearly so others can understand him/her				
2. Is able to follow oral directions				
3. Enjoys being read to				
4. Understands stories we read aloud				
5. "Reads" to me (telling about pictures and/or the story)				
6. Tries to read words in real life (street signs, cereal boxes, store signs)				
7. Draws pictures and writes some letters				
8. Writes in invented spelling				
9. Likes to tell about what he/she writes				

At home my child enjoys:

I have questions about:

_____
Parent

My Child as a Language Learner
Parent Observation (Grades 2–3)

Child's Name _____ Date _____ Grade _____

Please tell us about your child's language learning in the following areas. Please feel free to comment. We appreciate your insights as we work together with your child.

My Child:	Usually	Some-times	Rarely	Comments
1. Initiates and enjoys conversations with friends and adults				
2. Listens and responds appropriately to others				
3. Follows multi-step directions				
4. Enjoys being read to				
5. Chooses to read independently				
6. Tries to read unknown words by using:				
• Meaning				
• Picture clues				
• Letter/sound relationships				
7. Can retell story in own words				
8. Checks out books from school and public libraries				
9. Chooses to write independently • Stories, poems				
• Notes, lists, signs				
10. Likes to talk about and share his/her writing				
11. Uses invented and conventional spellings				

At home my child enjoys:

I have questions about:

_____
Parent

My Child as a Language Learner

Parent Observation (Grades 4–6)

Child's Name _____ Date _____ Grade _____

Please tell us about your child's language learning in the following areas. Please feel free to comment. We appreciate your insights as we work together with your child.

My Child:	Usually	Some-times	Rarely	Comments
1. Listens and responds appropriately to others				
2. Understands and responds to complex directions				
3. Understands and discusses story lines, characters, and themes with the family				
4. Cooses to read a variety of material independently: • for enjoyment (fiction, poetry)				
• for information (magazines, non-fiction)				
5. Chooses to write independently • Stories, poems				
• Lists, notes, letters				
6. Checks out books from school and public library				

At home my child enjoys:

I have questions about:

_____
Parent

Parent Reflection ·
Post-Conference Evaluation

WHO?

With some adaptations, these suggestions will guide all elementary and middle school students in self-contained classrooms, their parents, and teachers toward successful three-way conferences.

WHY?

Knowing that self-reflection and a sense of control over one's own destiny are key elements in building self-esteem, many school districts are increasing the involvement of students in parent-teacher conferences. Including the child in the conference helps to focus attention on the child in relation to the goals and the curriculum, rather than allowing curriculum issues to dominate. Three-way conferences offer a means for increased communication, but they require careful planning on the part of all participants. Following are the steps to be taken before the conference occurs.

HOW?

THE ROLE OF THE STUDENT

1. Write a letter to parents inviting them to come to school for a classroom observation. The letter also includes the scheduled conference time (ideally held after the classroom observation). An RSVP form is included. Students whose writing is less developed can sign and illustrate a letter written by the teacher.

2. Review his or her portfolio, making sure that its contents are reflective of the story the student wishes to tell about his or her own learning.

3. Prepare a self-report to accompany the portfolio. This self-report might include a reflection on how things are going at school (what is going well and what could be better), personal inventory of interests and strengths; information about the student's perception of his or her preferred learning styles (I learn best when ...); or a list of goals and a plan for achieving them. Students with less developed literacy skills could draw about things they think are going well or things they want to work on. Other students might be more comfortable tape-recording these ideas.

THE ROLE OF THE TEACHER

1. Provide opportunities for students to practice making introductions and leading discussions. These sessions could include a focus on interaction management: eye communication, body language, conversational turn taking, using appropriate volume and tone, active listening, etc. Role playing potential conferences gives the students a better understanding of how the conference might proceed and a sense of what it feels like to be in a leadership role. It is also very helpful to demonstrate the difference between advocating for yourself and defending yourself.

2. Assist students in developing a plan for the conference process (taking coats, introducing parents, opening the conference, etc.).

3. Communicate to parents and any other participants that the child will be taking a role as an active participant, not a passive listener.

4. Provide information for parents on how they can support learning at home.

THE ROLE OF THE PARENT

1.   Complete a **Parent Reflection** form and bring it to the conference. This form may be partially completed at home and expanded if the parents participate in a classroom observation.

2.   Talk with the student about messages he or she would like the parent to be sure to share during the conference.

3.   Prepare a list of questions and issues to bring to the conference.

DURING THE CONFERENCE

The teacher should (1) facilitate the setting of learning goals, (2) redirect conversations to include the student at any point where the student seems to be left out, (3) summarize the conference, (4) mention any unresolved issues needing further action or discussion, and (5) restate what each member of the group has agreed to do to support the learning of the student.

AFTER THE CONFERENCE

All participants fill out a **Post-Conference Evaluation** form reflecting aspects of the conference that went well, new information that seemed particularly informative, things to keep in mind at the next conference, etc. (Teachers could take dictation for students who are not able to complete the form independently.) The teacher leads a short debriefing session with the student to assess conference strengths and weaknesses that need to be remembered for the next time. The teacher's notes on this debriefing are added to a file and retained for the next conference. The child sends a note or picture to thank the parent(s) for attending.

WHAT ELSE?

Remember that developing a three-way, interactive conference is a developmental process for all participants. The first conferences may not be perfect; the goal is to improve with each attempt.

See: REPORTING pp. 222, 224

Parent Reflection and Post-Conference Evaluation were developed by Linda Hoyt, a Chapter I Coordinator for Beaverton Schools in Beaverton, OR.

Parent Reflection

What are some special things about your child that you could tell me?

What changes have you noticed in your child this year?

Please fill out the grid below, sharing information about your child at home as well as your perception of your child at school. Please feel free to add information that reflects your observation in the classroom.

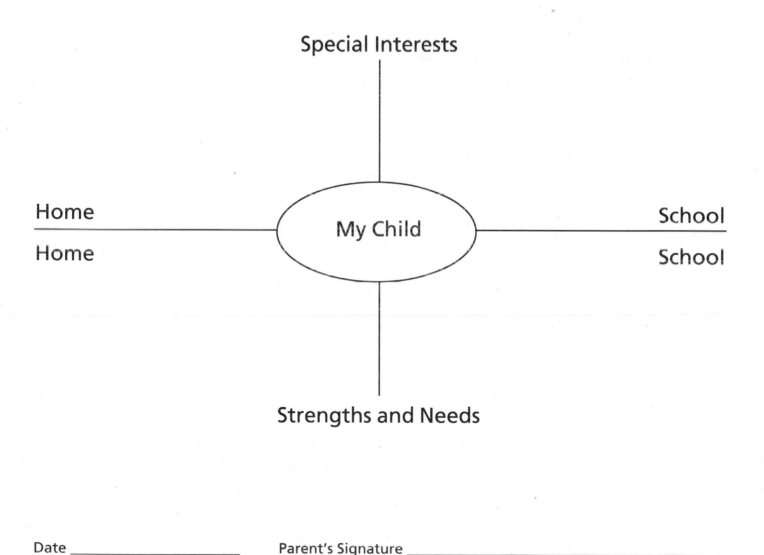

Special Interests

Home   School

Home   School

My Child

Strengths and Needs

Date _____   Parent's Signature _____

Post-Conference Evaluation

for

| STUDENT ☐ | PARENT ☐ | TEACHER ☐ |

Name _____ Date _____

What were the strengths of the conference?

What changes might we make in our next conference?

What insight did you gain as a result of this conference?

What goal will you set for yourself as a result of this conference?

Author Index

Altoff, Christina, 202
Anderson, Pam, 9
Bird, Lois Bridges, 40, 169, 219
Brooks, Nancy, 49, 55, 191
Burke, Carolyn, 99, 151
Caprio, Mark, 210
Chapnick, Greg, 177
Ching, Jann Pataray, 177
Collom, Jack, 169
Craven, Betty-Ann, 226
Crowell, Caryl G., 57
Curry, Toby Kahn, 183, 204, 212, 216
Dalrymple, Karen Sabers, 32
Der Mugrdechian, Katherine, 53
Elliott, Cynthia B., 24
Foley, Joan, 84
Goodman, Debra, 14, 37, 43, 149, 151, 173, 183, 186, 193, 212
Goodman, Yetta M., 47, 102, 104, 111, 151, 160, 163
Hagan, Michael, 145
Hartle-Schutte, David, 74, 90
Hebert, Elizabeth A. Y., 222, 224
Hood, Wendy, 18
Howard, Catherine P., 127
Hoyt, Linda, 235
Hysmith, Cecilia, 93
Kitagawa, Mary M., 71
Lamme, Linda Leonard, 93
Lowell Elementary School, 81, 166, 228
Luke, Carlen, 49
Manning, Gary, 143
Manning, Maryann, 143
Marchand, Pat, 214
Marek, Ann, 163
Mazzuchi, Diana, 49, 55, 191
Mickelson, Norma I., 127
Miller, Howard M., 206
Ogren, Denise, 116
PAUSD, 20, 32, 62, 123, 231
Raines, Bonnie, 200
Regnier, Mary Jo, 186
Ruddiman, Joan, 118
Seil, Anne B., 214
Shine, Maggie, 49, 55, 191
Siu-Runyan, Yvonne, 134
Truesdale, Laura S., 181
Tucson TAWL, 99, 141
Walker, Avery D., 35, 118, 166, 198
Watson, Dorothy, 151
Weaver, Connie, 157
White, Maureen, 14, 26, 28, 30, 81, 121, 123, 181
Whitin, Phyllis, 202
Wortman, Robert C., 131
Zinke, Sharon, 69

Title Index

A

A Process Checklist for Writing, 81 **82**
Analyze an Author, 183 **185**
Anecdotal Observation Sheet, 49 **52**
Anecdotal Records, 53 **54**
Assessing the Spelling Levels of Young Children, 143 **144**
Author/Illustrator Study, 183 **184**

B

Book Review: Fiction Books, 186 **187**
Book Review: Non-Fiction Books, 186 **188**
Book Review: Picture Books, 186 **189**
Bookhandling Knowledge Task, 104 **105-110**
Burke Reading Interview, 99 **100**

C

Center Committee Plans, 37 **39**
Child's Concepts of Reading, 111 **112-113**
Child's Concepts of Written and Pictorial Representation, 111 **114-115**
Children Learn to Read by Reading, 24 **25**
Classroom Community of Readers, 118 **119**
Complete Anecdotal Form, 49 **50-51**
Conventions of Print, 145 **148**
Cumulative Writing Folder/Kindergarten, 74 **75**
Cumulative Writing Folder/Grade 1, 74 **76**
Cumulative Writing Folder/Grade 2, 74 **77**
Cumulative Writing Folder/Grade 3, 74 **78**
Cumulative Writing Folder/Grade 4, 74 **79**
Cumulative Writing Folder/Grade 5, 74 **80**

D

Developing a Reading Profile, 149 **150**
Development of Narrative/Expository, 145 **146**

E

Editing Checklist, 166 **167**
Evaluation of Discussion Groups, 206 **208**
Evaluation of Group Projects, 206 **209**

F

Fall Math Assessment, 84 **88**
Fall Reading and Writing Assessment, 84 **86**
Fostering Student Self-Evaluation: Focus on Writing, 200 **201**

G

General Procedure for Marking Miscues, 151 **152**
Getting Started with Portfolios, 219 **220-221**
Getting to Know Your Child, 127 **130**
Growth Portfolio Rationale, 228 **229**

H

Help the Author, 123 **126**
Home and School Independent Reading/Grades K–1, 20 **21**
Home and School Independent Reading/Grades 2–3, 20 **22**
Home and School Independent Reading/Grades 4–5, 20 **23**
HOPS: Pre-Observation Conference, 134 **135**
HOPS: Classroom Observation, 134 **136**
HOPS: Written Feedback, 134 **137**
How Well Did We Work Together?, 191 **192**

K

Kidwatching Guidelines, 47 **48**

L

Language Arts Review, 138 **139-140**
Learning Experiences Form, 224 **225**
Learning How to Learn a Second Language, 210 **211**
Learning Logs (sample), 175 **176**
Library Bookmark, 14 **16**
Listening Post Book Review, 186 **190**
Literacy Environment Evaluation, 90 **91-92**
Literature Circles, 177 **180**
Literature Response Guide, 177 **179**
Literature Studies Guidelines, 177 **178**
Looking Closer at a Writing Sample, 173 **174**

M

Miscue Analysis Form, 157 **159**
Miscue Analysis Procedure IV Individual Conference Form, 151 **154**
Miscue Analysis Procedure III Questions, 151 **153**
Miscue Analysis: Retelling Summary, 160 **162**
My Child as a Language Learner/Grades K–1, 231 **232**
My Child as a Language Learner/Grades 2–3, 231 **233**
My Child as a Language Learner/Grades 4–6, 231 **234**
My Ideas for Writing, 28 **29**
My Plans, 37 **38**
My Reading Records, 14 **15**

O

Observed Reading Behavior, 84 **85**
Oral Language Evaluation, 141 **142**
Outstanding Poetic Qualities, 169 **172**

P

Parent Observation, 55 **56**
Parent Reflection, 235 **237**
Parent Response Form, 216 **218**
Parent-Student Questionnaire, 127 **128-129**
Peer Conferencing, 123 **124**
Peer Conferencing Guidelines, 123 **125**
Peer Editing Checklist, 166 **168**
Planning Grid for Thematic Study, 43 **45-46**
Planning Grid for Thematic Study (sample), 43 **44**
Portfolio Assessment: Self-Evaluation Sheet, 226 **227**
Portfolio Evenings: Guiding Questions, 222 **223**
Post-Conference Evaluation, 235 **238**
Primary Developmental Checklist, 9 **10-13**
Primary Writing Goals, 81 **83**

Principal's Goals for the Classroom, 131 **133**
Principal's Goals for the School, 131 **132**
Profile of Language Arts Outcomes/Grades K–1, 62 **63-64**
Profile of Language Arts Outcomes/Grades 2–3, 62 **65-66**
Profile of Language Arts Outcomes/Grades 4–5, 62 **67-68**
Profile of Reading Strategy Use, 151 **156**

Q

Qualities of Effective Writing, 169 **171**
Quarterly Growth Summary, 228 **230**

R

Reader's-Writer's Reflections, 181 **181**
Reader-Selected Miscues, 151 **155**
Reading: A Guide for Observation, 69 **70**
Reading Contract, 18 **19**
Reading Environmental Print, 102 **103**
Reading in Kindergarten, 116 **117**
Reading Interest Inventory, 99 **101**
Reading Log, 14 **17**
Reading Record for Conferences, 93 **98**
Reading Strategies, 145 **147**
Research Contract, 40 **41**
Responding to Assignments: Self-Evaluation, 198 **199**
Responding to Literature, 181 **182**
Response to Literature Scale, 93 **97**
Retrospective and Collaborative Miscue Analysis, 163 **165**

S

Scale of Emergent Reading, 93 **96**
Scale of Writing Development, 93 **95**
Self-Evaluation Across the Curriculum: Language Arts, 193 **197**
Self-Evaluation Across the Curriculum: Math, 193 **195**
Self-Evaluation Across the Curriculum: Overview, 193 **194**
Self-Evaluation Across the Curriculum: Science, 193 **196**
Self-Evaluation in a Graduate Course, 212 **213**
Semester Update (sample letter), 216 **217-218**
Showing You Know, 40 **42**
Something to Write Home About (sample letter), 202 **203**
Spelling Discovery, 35 **36**
Story Response, 118 **120**
Student Writing Survey/Interest Inventory, 121 **122**
Survey in the Language Arts: Reading, 71 **72**
Survey in the Language Arts: Writing, 71 **73**

T

Teacher Self-Evaluation, 214 **215**
Thinking About Myself as a Learner, 204 **205**

W

Weekly Discussion Group Evaluation, 206 **207**
Whole Language Checklist, 57 **58-61**
Winter Math Assessment, 84 **89**
Winter Reading and Writing Assessment, 84 **87**
Writing Process Overview, 26 **27**
Writing Record, 32 **33**
Writing Workshop Report, 32 **34**
Writing Workshop: Status of the Class, 30 **31**